SEPUP
Issue-Oriented Science

ISSUES AND EARTH SCIENCE

Geological Processes

THIRD EDITION
REDESIGNED FOR THE NGSS

SEPUP
Issue-Oriented Science

ISSUES AND
EARTH SCIENCE

Geological Processes

THIRD EDITION

REDESIGNED FOR THE NGSS

THE LAWRENCE HALL OF SCIENCE
UNIVERSITY OF CALIFORNIA, BERKELEY

This book is part of SEPUP's *Issues and Science* course sequence. For more information about this sequence, see the SEPUP and Lab-Aids websites.

ISSUES AND EARTH SCIENCE

ISSUES AND LIFE SCIENCE

ISSUES AND PHYSICAL SCIENCE

Additional SEPUP instructional materials include
SEPUP Modules: Grades 6–12
Science and Sustainability: Course for Grades 9–12
Science and Global Issues: Biology: Course for High School Biology

This material is based in part upon work supported by the National Science Foundation under Grant 0099265. Any opinions, findings, and conclusions or recommendations expressed in this material are those of the authors and do not necessarily reflect the views of the National Science Foundation.

For photo and illustration credits, see page 163, which constitutes an extension of this copyright page.

The preferred citation format for this book is SEPUP. (2018). *Issues and Earth Science: Geological Processes*. Lawrence Hall of Science, University of California at Berkeley. Ronkonkoma, NY: Lab-Aids, Inc.

Third Edition

Q1 2 3 4 5 6 7 8 9   22 21 20 19 18

ISBN: 978-1-63093-479-8
v1

SEPUP
Lawrence Hall of Science
University of California at Berkeley
Berkeley CA 94720-5200

email: sepup@berkeley.edu
website: www.sepuplhs.org

Published by

LaB-aiDS

17 Colt Court
Ronkonkoma NY 11779
Website: www.lab-aids.com

A Letter to *Issues and Earth Science* Students

As you examine the activities in this book, you may wonder, "Why does this book look so different from other science books I've seen?" The reason is simple: it is a different kind of science program, and only some of what you will learn can be seen by leafing through this book!

Issues and Earth Science uses several kinds of activities to teach science. As you conduct these activities, you will engage in the same practices used by scientists to understand the natural world and by engineers to solve problems. For example, you will investigate how water moves through different materials. You will map the locations of volcanoes and earthquakes, and will examine how the Earth's surface has moved in the past and is moving now. A combination of laboratories, investigations, readings, models, simulations, and discussions will help you develop your understanding of science and the relevance of earth science to your interests.

You will find that important scientific ideas come up again and again in different activities throughout the program. You will be expected to do more than just memorize these concepts: you will be asked to develop explanations and apply them to solve problems. In particular, you will improve your decision-making skills by using evidence to weigh outcomes and to decide what you think should be done about the scientific issues facing our society.

How do we know that this is a good way for you to learn? In general, research on science education supports it. In particular, many of the activities in this book were tested by hundreds of students and their teachers, and then modified on the basis of their feedback. New activities are based on what we learned in classrooms using the materials and on new research on science learning. In a sense, this entire book is the result of an investigation: we had people test our ideas, we interpreted the results, and we then revised our ideas! We believe the result will show you that learning more about science is important, enjoyable, and relevant to your life.

SEPUP Staff

ISSUES & EARTH SCIENCE THIRD EDITION

Director: Barbara Nagle

Co-Director: John Howarth

Coordinator: Janet Bellantoni

AUTHORS

Sara R. Walkup, Katrina M. Arras, Roger Groom, John Howarth, Manisha Hariani

CONTENT AND SCIENTIFIC REVIEW

Dr. Anne E. Egger, Director, Office of Undergraduate Research and Associate Professor, Geological Sciences and Science Education, Central Washington University, Ellensburg, Washington

PRODUCTION

Coordination, Design, Photo Research, Composition: Seventeenth Street Studios

Production Coordinator for Lab-Aids: Hethyr Tregerman

Editing: Kerry Ouellet

FIELD TEST CENTERS

The classroom is SEPUP's laboratory for development. We are extremely appreciative of the following center directors and teachers who taught the program during the 2003–04 and 2004–05 school years. These teachers and their students contributed significantly to improving the first edition of the course. Since then, *Issues and Earth Science* has been used in thousands of classrooms across the United States. This third edition is based on what we have learned from teachers and students in those classrooms. It also includes new data and information, so the issues included in the course remain fresh and up-to-date.

ATLANTA, GEORGIA

Geeta Verma, *Center Director*
Felecia Bell, Wanda Ellis, Lillian Harris, Patricia Lewis, Millicent McCaskill, Demetra McCoy, Melanie Robinson, Nicole Satchell

BUFFALO, NEW YORK

Kathaleen Burke, *Center Director*
Delores Anderson, Dianne Johnson, Deborah Kimble, Steven Koch, Corean Lofton

DALY CITY, CALIFORNIA

Andrew Coblentz, *Center Director*
Andrew Coblentz, Ken Klein, Catherine Macay, Benjamin Moser, Lucy Schoening

GREELEY-EVANS, COLORADO

Ray Tschillard, *Center Director*
Joann Angus, Djems Domerson, Nick Durham, Christina Kauffman, Jason McLaughlin, Gemarie Romero, Ruby Sabzevari, Mark Wiegers

LEMON GROVE, CALIFORNIA

Samantha Swann, *Center Director*
Jennifer Bates, Jim Haynes, Linda Schultz, Patti Sherillo, John Tessier

PINELLAS COUNTY, FLORIDA

Dr. Chin-Tang Liu and Nancy Stitt, *Center Directors*
Shirley Green, Lisa Mackey, Jennifer Sinphay, Nancy Stitt

WAKE COUNTY, NORTH CAROLINA

Michael Tally, Kim Gervase, and Catherine Norris, *Center Directors*
James Akins, Jon Corcoran, Karen Farnham, Jennifer Koch, Carla Steger

WINSTON-SALEM/FORSYTH COUNTY, NORTH CAROLINA

Jim Bott, *Center Director*
Amelie Bartolino, Ed Beiles, Mary Kay Bell, John Cardarelli, Megan Clayton, Jennifer Sasser, Barbara Strange, Jane Trace

VISTA, CALIFORNIA

Donna Markey, *Center Director*
Amy Alexander, Melissa Boeche, Nicole Buchanan, Dorothy Jones, Stacy Robe, Zamaria Rocio

Contents

Geological Processes

NAYELI AND IZAIAH *were very excited to see each other on the first day of school. Nayeli couldn't wait to tell Izaiah about his summer trip to see his grandparents and their visit to Mount Saint Helens in Washington State.*

"Izaiah, Mt. St. Helens was amazing! Did you know that it had a huge eruption in 1980, and the side and top of the mountain blew off? It used to be a beautiful cone-shaped mountain surrounded by forests, and now there's a huge hole in the top and still no trees. It sent ash into the atmosphere that traveled all over the world!" Nayeli explained.

"Whoa," responded Izaiah. "Could you imagine seeing that in real life? Do you think it's going to erupt again?"

"Well," said Nayeli, "the park ranger said that it had a small eruption in 2004. What's amazing is that they knew something was up because they measured more earthquakes under the mountain. And the only reason the mountain is there in the first place is because of a lot of eruptions building it up over a super long time."

Izaiah pondered for a moment. "But wait! My grandparents live near Mt. Hood in Oregon, which is near Mt. St. Helens. Now I'm worried!"

• • •

What causes volcanic eruptions and earthquakes? Is one likely to occur where you live? How can we use technology to monitor the movement of Earth's surface? How do natural hazards, like volcanoes, earthquakes, and landslides, affect the people who live near them? How do changes on Earth's surface affect the availability of natural resources?

In this unit, you will explain how geological processes cause gradual and sudden changes to Earth's surface. You will analyze and interpret data to explain how the Earth's surface has changed over geological time. You will use and develop models to investigate how different kinds of rocks and natural resources form as a result of geological processes.

1 *Storing Nuclear Waste*

EACH YEAR, THE United States produces between 2,000 and 2,400 metric tons of nuclear waste at nuclear power plants. **Nuclear waste** is the leftover radioactive material produced by nuclear reactors. Radioactive materials radiate energy, some of which is harmful. It can't be seen, felt, or heard, but it can damage living cells and cause diseases, such as cancer. Currently, most nuclear waste is stored at the power plants where it is produced. If the containers storing nuclear waste were to leak, it could be released into the air or nearby bodies of water. This could be dangerous for people living nearby who breathe the air and interact with the water. Individuals who inhale or ingest radioactive materials are more likely to develop radiation-related illnesses than people who do not. The level of risk depends on the dose and length of exposure to radiation.

For more than 50 years, scientists have been considering ways to store nuclear waste safely. They have proposed sending it into space, placing it in the ocean floor, and burying it on a remote island. But those options all pose problems. Most experts now agree that the safest solution is to store nuclear waste in containers engineered to contain the waste and place them in a central location deep underground. In January 2012, a group of experts appointed by the president, called the Commission on America's Nuclear Future, recommended that the country should find and develop one or more deep underground storage sites. In order to pursue this recommendation, there are many scientific and social issues involved in choosing a site for nuclear waste storage.

Electricity is generated at a nuclear power plant.

GUIDING QUESTION

What factors must be considered when deciding where to store nuclear waste?

MATERIALS

For each student

    1   Student Sheet 1.1, "Considering Where to Store Nuclear Waste"

PROCEDURE

Part A: Reading about Nuclear Waste

1. With your group, read the background information about nuclear waste on the pages that follow. Have each person read one section aloud.

2. Based on the background information you read, discuss what you would look for in a site to store nuclear waste.

   Remember to listen to and consider the ideas of the other members of your group. If you disagree with others in your group, explain why you disagree.

Background Information about Nuclear Waste

Where is nuclear waste generated?

Reactors create nuclear waste at nuclear power plants, nuclear medical treatment facilities, and nuclear research and technology facilities. The materials have high to low levels of radioactivity depending on the technology they are used for. Nuclear reactors at power plants and government defense projects generate the most nuclear waste. Most of it is in the form of highly radioactive solids made of metal, ceramic, or glass. Some of these solids will remain radioactive for a few years, but others are likely to remain radioactive for at least 250,000 years.

How are people protected from nuclear waste?

The most likely danger from nuclear waste is the accidental release of radiation into the air or water, where it can spread through the environment and might be ingested or inhaled. Nuclear waste is stored in containers made of lead, steel, and concrete to protect people from its harmful effects and to prevent it from leaking into air and water supplies. The containers are built to resist impact, high temperatures, and corrosive chemicals. However, water is present everywhere underground, and it is possible that water could damage these containers over long periods of time and cause them to leak. Thus, experts have determined that it is best to store nuclear waste containers in dry areas with little rainfall.

How much waste comes from nuclear power plants?

The United States has 99 operating nuclear reactors at 60 power plants. About 20% of the electricity in the United States comes from these power plants. Over time, they have produced more than 70,000 metric tons of nuclear waste. If these reactors continue to operate and no additional nuclear power plants are built, the amount of nuclear waste to store will be over 140,000 metric tons by the year 2050. If more plants are built to help meet our electricity demands, this number would increase.

A nuclear power plant

How is nuclear waste stored now?

Nuclear waste is currently stored at 75 sites in 33 states. When nuclear fuel is first removed from reactors, it is placed in deep pools of water. The water helps to cool the fuel and protect workers from radiation. About 50,000 metric tons of nuclear waste is currently stored in pools. At some power plants, the cooled nuclear waste is transferred to dry storage. About 15,000 metric tons of nuclear waste is currently stored in dry containers above ground. Nuclear experts believe that it is possible to create places hundreds of meters (m) below Earth's surface where up to 70,000 metric tons of nuclear waste can be safely stored for at least 10,000 years.

Nuclear power plants use radioactive fuel rods. When these rods can no longer be used to produce energy, they are first placed in pools of water to cool.

Part B: Analyzing Maps

3. Examine the two maps below and on the following page: "Population Density by County" and "U.S. Locations of Operating Nuclear Reactors." Describe the patterns you notice in the data presented on the maps with your group. Then, discuss how these data influences your thinking about where to store nuclear waste.

4. Record your ideas about how the data from the two maps would inform your decision about where to store nuclear waste on Student Sheet 1.1, "Considering Where to Store Nuclear Waste." In the first column, write the two considerations about which you gathered data from the maps: human population density and locations of operating nuclear reactors. In the second column, write the action you would recommend in regard to each consideration. Explain why you would recommend taking this action when deciding where to store nuclear waste.

5. In your group of four students, discuss and share your ideas from Student Sheet 1.1.

Population Density by County in the Contiguous U.S.

Average number of people/square mile
- 300.0 or more
- 200.0 to 299.9
- 100.0 to 199.9
- 50.0 to 99.9
- 10.0 to 49.9
- Fewer than 10.0

Locations of Operating Nuclear Reactors in the Contiguous U.S.

ANALYSIS

1. Do you think that storing nuclear waste in one or two sites deep in the ground would be better than the current situation where nuclear waste is stored at the sites where it is produced? Explain by

   a. stating your decision.

   b. supporting your decision with as many pieces of evidence as you can. **Evidence** is factual information or data that support or refute a claim

   c. discussing the trade-offs of your decision. A **trade-off** is a desirable outcome given up to gain another desirable outcome.

2. What other information would you like to have before you make a decision about where to store nuclear waste? Be sure to explain how this information would be helpful.

3. Choose one of the recommended actions you described on Student Sheet 1.1. Are there any disadvantages associated with taking this action? Explain why or why not.

4. As you learned in this activity, advances in technology often lead to advances in science. Sometimes they also lead to new challenges.

    a. In what ways has the development of nuclear energy led to advances as well as challenges for society?

    b. What other developments in technology have led to advances as well as challenges for people?

EXTENSION

In 1987, the U.S. government selected Yucca Mountain in southern Nevada as an underground storage site for nuclear waste. However, in 2011, government officials decided not to build there. Visit the *SEPUP Third Edition Geological Processes* page of the SEPUP website at *www.sepuplhs.org/middle/third-edition* for links to more information about the long-term storage of nuclear waste at Yucca Mountain. What new questions do you have about the long-term storage of nuclear waste?

2 *Investigating Groundwater*

INVESTIGATION

As **YOU LEARNED** in the previous activity, one factor that might influence where nuclear waste can be stored deep underground is the amount of rainfall in an area. Why? Because precipitation that falls on land may fall or flow into lakes, rivers, or oceans, but a lot of this water will pass through the soil and into the underlying rocks below Earth's surface. Water that goes beneath Earth's surface is called **groundwater.**

In this activity, you will explore how water enters and flows underground through earth materials. This information might be helpful as you consider where to store nuclear waste.

Hydrologists preparing equipment to take groundwater samples below Earth's surface

GUIDING QUESTION

How does water interact with earth materials?

MATERIALS

For each group of four students

> 1 clear plastic cup (9-ounce) of clay
> 1 clear plastic cup (9-ounce) of sand
> 1 clear plastic cup (9-ounce) of water
> paper towels

For each pair of students

> 1 plastic spoon
> 2 graduated cups (30-mL)
> 1 magnifying lens
> 1 SEPUP tray
> 2 tube holders for SEPUP tray
> 2 clear plastic tubes with a hole in the middle of the closed end
> stopwatch or view of wall clock

For each student

> 1 Student Sheet 1.1, "Considering Where to Store Nuclear Waste"

SAFETY

Be careful when handling the clay material. Do not inhale the clay dust or place the clay dust near your eyes. Wash your hands after completing the activity.

PROCEDURE

1. In your science notebook, make a data table like the one below. Make the spaces big enough to include drawings of the earth materials.

Observations of Clay and Sand

Tube containing	Observations before adding water	Observations after adding water

2. Examine the samples of clay and sand using the magnifying lens. Record your description of the size and shape of the particles for each sample in your data table.

3. Fill one of the graduated cups to the 30-mL mark with clay using the plastic spoon.

4. Carefully pour the clay into one of the clear plastic tubes. Hold your finger over the small hole in the bottom of the tube as you pour.

5. Fill the other graduated cup to the 30-mL mark with sand using the plastic spoon.

6. Carefully pour the sand into the other clear plastic tube. Hold your finger over the hole in the bottom as you pour.

7. Place the bottom of the tube of sand in a tube holder. Place the tube and tube holder with the open end up over the large cup B in the SEPUP tray. Place the bottom of the tube of clay in the other tube holder. Place the tube and tube holder with the open end up over the large cup C in the SEPUP tray.

8. Add 15 mL of water to each of the graduated cups.

9. Note the time (or start the stopwatch) as you and your partner simultaneously add water to each tube as shown below. Make sure to pour the water slowly and carefully.

10. For the next 5 minutes (min), observe what happens to the water in each tube. Record your observations in the final column of your data table.

11. Discuss the similarities and differences in your observations for clay and sand before and after adding the water.

12. Follow your teacher's directions for cleanup.

ANALYSIS

1. **Sediments** are parts of rocks, shells, and dead organisms that have been worn down into small pieces, mostly by the effects of water. The earth materials you used in the activity—sand and clay—are sediments. Sediments settle on top of each other. The layers they form are pressed and glued together. Over long periods of time, these layers of hardened sediment form **sedimentary rock.**

    a. What do you think happens when water flows from Earth's surface into a shale rock layer, which is made of clay sediments?

    b. What do you think happens when water flows from Earth's surface into a sandstone rock layer, which is made of sand sediments?

2. An **aquifer** is a rock layer that allows groundwater to flow through it. An **aquitard** is a rock layer that restricts the flow of groundwater.

    a. Draw a diagram to show how you would use the materials from this activity (clay, sand, water, and a plastic tube) to build a model of an aquifer.

    b. How would your placement of the earth materials in the tube allow water to flow and collect in an aquifer?

    c. Which earth material would be considered an aquitard?

3. The world's aquifers store much more freshwater underground than is stored in all the lakes and rivers on Earth's surface. Aquifers are sources of drinking water for many people. Add the consideration "location of aquifers" in a new row on Student Sheet 1.1, "Considering Where to Store Nuclear Waste." In the second column, write the recommended action you would take in regard to this consideration. Explain why you recommend taking this action when deciding where to store nuclear waste.

EXTENSION 1

Use the earth materials, water, and a plastic tube to build the model of an aquifer you drew in Analysis item 2. Describe what you did and what happened.

3 Modeling Landslides

VIEW AND REFLECT

RAINFALL CAN REPLENISH groundwater and aquifers. It can also cause natural hazards that may result in considerable damage. A **natural hazard** is a natural event that may negatively affect people and the environment. A **landslide** is the flow of rock, soil, and other earth materials down a slope. Landslides often happen during or after long or heavy periods of rainfall. In this activity, you will learn how scientists built a model to study landslides. A **model** is any representation of a system (or its components) used to help one understand and communicate how it works.

Landslides can destroy everything in their path. It is important to consider landslide risk when deciding where to store nuclear waste.

GUIDING QUESTION

How can a natural hazard create challenges for storing nuclear waste?

This landslide occurred in a mountainous area of Puerto Rico in 2017, as a result of heavy rainfall during Hurricane Maria.

MATERIALS

For each student

    1 Student Sheet 3.1, "Anticipation Guide: Landslide Video"

    1 Student Sheet 1.1, "Considering Where to Store Nuclear Waste"

PROCEDURE

1. Use Student Sheet 3.1, "Anticipation Guide: Landslide Video," to prepare yourself for watching the video.

2. Watch the video about landslides.

3. Return to Student Sheet 3.1, and complete the "After" column by marking whether you agree (+) or disagree (–) with each statement. Under each statement, explain how the activity gave evidence to support or change your ideas.

ANALYSIS

1. Think about what you learned from watching the video. How did using a model help scientists understand what happens during a landslide?

2. Why might it be important to consider landslide risk when deciding where to store nuclear waste? Use evidence from the activity to support your ideas.

EXTENSION

What can people do to prepare for a landslide? Visit the *SEPUP Third Edition Geological Processes* page of the SEPUP website at *www. sepuplhs.org/middle/third-edition*, and go to the Landslide Preparedness link to learn how to be ready for a landslide. What would you recommend to a friend about how to be prepared for a landslide?

4 Natural Hazards Caused by Earthquakes and Volcanoes

WHEN SELECTING A site to store nuclear waste, it is important to identify risks of natural hazards caused by earthquakes or volcanoes. An **earthquake** is a sudden release of energy in Earth's interior, which can cause shaking at the surface. A **volcano** is an opening in Earth's surface through which lava, gas, and ash escape from magma underground. **Magma** is hot liquid rock under Earth's surface. Earthquakes and volcanoes can cause natural hazards. If these events were to take place near a nuclear waste storage facility, they could present problems for the safe storage of radioactive material.

GUIDING QUESTION

What natural hazards are caused by earthquakes and volcanic eruptions?

The smallest type of volcano is called a cinder cone. In many cases, cinder cones form on the sides of a larger volcano. The photo above shows a cinder cone on Mount Etna in Italy.

During earthquakes, blocks of rock move along a fracture called a fault. The deep line shown in the middle of the picture on the left shows one of the best-known faults in the United States—the San Andreas Fault in California.

MATERIALS

For each student

1   Student Sheet 4.1, "Directed Reading Table: Natural Hazards Caused by Earthquakes and Volcanoes"

1   Student Sheet 1.1, "Considering Where to Store Nuclear Waste"

PROCEDURE

1. Below you will find four reading passages about four different earthquakes or sites of volcanic activity and the natural hazards they have caused. Decide with your group which of the passages each student will read.

2. Read your assigned passage individually. Complete the row for your reading passage on Student Sheet 4.1, "Directed Reading Table: Natural Hazards Caused by Earthquakes and Volcanoes," as you read.

3. When everyone in your group has finished reading and taking notes on their sheets, take turns sharing what you have learned with your group members. As your group members share, be sure to listen carefully, and record information about each event on the remaining rows of Student Sheet 4.1.

The 2010 Haitian Earthquake: Ground-Shaking

On January 12, 2010, a strong earthquake shook the Republic of Haiti. This earthquake happened about 25 kilometers (km) southwest of the capital, Port-au-Prince. Haiti's population was 9.6 million. More than 316,000 people were killed or missing and presumed dead, 300,000 were injured, and over 1.3 million lost their homes. The cost of the damage was estimated between 7 to 14 billion U.S. dollars.

Many buildings in Haiti were not designed or built to withstand intense ground-shaking during an earthquake. It was estimated that about 300,000 homes collapsed or were badly damaged in the country. Also, many structures housing

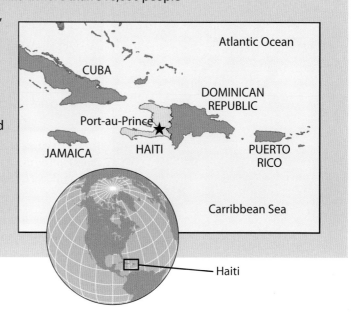

key services, such as hospitals, schools, and government buildings, were severely damaged or destroyed. The city of Léogâne [LAY-oh-zhahn] was closest to the source of the earthquake. The ground shaking damaged or destroyed 80–90% of the buildings.

These images show a hospital in Port-au-Prince before and after the earthquake.

In areas where earthquakes happen a lot, such as Haiti, new buildings can be designed and built to lessen the risk of collapse during ground-shaking caused by earthquakes. Older buildings can be fixed to increase the chance that they will not collapse during an earthquake. One way governments ensure that buildings are safe is to adopt and enforce a building code. A building code provides standards for builders to follow as they build new buildings or fix old ones. These standards can ensure that the structures will withstand ground-shaking in the event of an earthquake. In the United States, local governments enforce the building code. However, adopting and enforcing a building code is very expensive. Ensuring that buildings are designed and built to be safe during an earthquake is a tremendous challenge in Haiti because it is one of the poorest countries in the world. At the time of the earthquake, Haiti did not have a national building code in place.

The 2015 Nepal Earthquake: Landslides

On April 25, 2015, a very strong earthquake shook Nepal. It was centered in Gorkha, Nepal. Gorkha is 82 km northwest of the capital city, Kathmandu. Scientists estimate that the earthquake may have caused between 10,000 and 60,000 landslides. Landslides are common in this mountainous area during the wet monsoon season. But these landslides occurred during the dry season when the land is most stable. The intense ground-shaking from the earthquake caused the rock, soil, and other earth materials to become unstable. Once the materials were unstable, gravity pulled them down the mountainous terrain.

One significant landslide caused by the earthquake happened nearly a month after the event. The earthquake in Gorkha, as well as another large earthquake that happened in the area on May 12, 2015, caused large cracks to form in the rock in a steep cliff above the village of Baisari. When rock began to fall from the cliff on May 22, 2015, the Nepal Army evacuated the area. A few days later, the cliff failed, which generated a large landslide. Huge amounts of earth materials flowing downslope from the cliff destroyed 27 buildings and buried the village. A nearby river flooded and formed a lake.

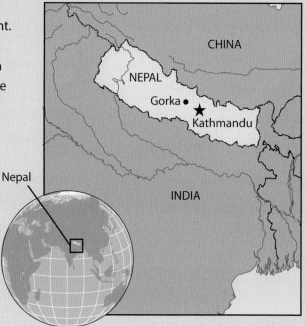

Scientists use a variety of equipment to monitor hillsides in areas where earthquakes happen a lot. One instrument the scientists put on the slopes in Nepal were seismometers [size-MOM-uh-ters]. Seismometers measure ground-shaking and allow scientists to gather data about how much the ground shakes in an area. They can use this information to determine how much ground-shaking it takes to cause a landslide. Their goal is to use the data to make better predictions of when and where landslides will happen. This is very challenging in Nepal because there are several different kinds of events that can trigger landslides. There are earthquakes, heavy rains, and steep slopes. This makes it hard to know where to build villages and towns in Nepal that will be safe from landslides.

A landslide caused by earthquakes in Nepal buried the village of Baisari.

The 1980 Volcanic Eruption of Mt. St. Helens: Ash Fall

On May 18, 1980, the Mt. St. Helens volcano in Washington State, USA, erupted violently, blasting gas and volcanic ash high up into the air. Volcanic ash is very small pieces of rock and volcanic glass that are ejected from a volcano during an eruption. Wind can carry these tiny particles very long distances, as far as hundreds or even thousands of kilometers from an eruption site. A few hours after Mt. St. Helens erupted, people in a town called Yakima, about 230 km (about 145 miles) east of the volcano, noticed dark clouds in the sky. As the dark clouds moved over the town, ash began to fall. The area was covered in as much as 10 centimeters (cm; 4 inches) of ash. By the end of the day, about 500 million metric tons of ash from the eruption at Mt. St. Helens had fallen across three states.

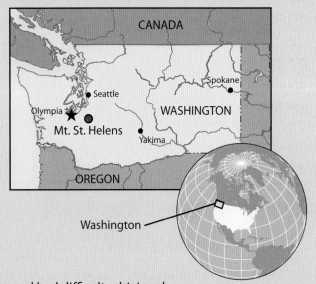

Washington

Volcanic ash falls cause many problems. After the 1980 eruption, roads in eastern Washington were closed. Drivers couldn't see and had difficulty driving due to the ash fall. Heavy ash fell on buildings. Roofs were at risk for collapse. Ash falls can also cause widespread power outages. Hospitals and other emergency services cannot respond quickly without electricity. There is also a high health risk for people when they breathe in volcanic ash. Children, seniors, and people with breathing problems, such as asthma, are especially at risk. Ash falls can also harm crops and livestock.

Scientists monitor active volcanoes using a variety of scientific equipment. There are early warning signs that a volcano may erupt. If these signs are observed, they can then warn the public. In the 1980 Mt. St. Helens eruption, scientists gathered data that showed that a significant volcanic eruption was likely. Areas close to the volcano were evacuated before the event.

Mt. St. Helens erupted violently in 1980.

Areas near active volcanoes can prepare for ash falls by developing plans for evacuation. They can also plan for emergency response teams to be ready for an eruption. People who live in these areas should prepare emergency kits. The kits should have supplies for a few days if they need to stay inside while the ash falls.

Mammoth Mountain: Volcanic Gas

Mammoth Mountain is a volcano located in California, USA. The volcano formed during a series of eruptions, and the last large eruption occurred about 57,000 years ago. Smaller eruptions continued since then, but the volcano hasn't erupted for many hundreds of years. There is still volcanic activity occurring on the mountain. In parts of the volcano, volcanic gases escape through layers of soil.

Magma releases water vapor, a harmless gas. But other volcanic gases can be dangerous for nearby organisms. At Mammoth Mountain, carbon dioxide gas is released from the magma underground and it rises through the soil. Carbon dioxide is denser than the air around it, so it collects in areas of low elevation. As the gas collects, it can reach high concentrations. High concentrations of carbon dioxide gas can be harmful to living things.

The carbon dioxide emitted from the magma in Mammoth Mountain is closely monitored. The gas can escape from underground for weeks, months, or years.

One area where the carbon dioxide is frequently measured is near Horseshoe Lake on the mountain. Many trees have died there. Monitoring these areas allows scientists to know when the level of this gas is unsafe. At those times, people must stay away from these areas. Scientists also use these data to create maps that show where the gas is escaping. They look for patterns in the amount of volcanic gas emitted over time. Collecting and analyzing data about the release of volcanic gas helps scientists better understand the volcanic activity happening at the mountain.

Trees killed by high concentrations of carbon dioxide gas at Mammoth Mountain

ANALYSIS

1. Look back at the facts about natural hazards caused by earthquakes and volcanoes from Student Sheet 4.1. Which of these natural hazards do you think presents the least challenge for the safe storage of nuclear waste underground? Explain your answer, making sure to use evidence to support your ideas.

2. Add the consideration "natural hazards caused by earthquakes and volcanoes" in a new row on Student Sheet 1.1, "Considering Where to Store Nuclear Waste." In the second column, write the recommended action you would take in regard to this consideration. Explain why you recommend taking this action when deciding where to store nuclear waste.

5 Modeling Volcanic Eruptions

MODELING

DURING A VOLCANIC eruption, magma from underground is released onto Earth's surface. Prior to eruption, magma is located in the magma chamber of a volcano beneath the volcano's opening in Earth's surface. When magma flows over Earth's surface, it is called **lava**. **Igneous rock** forms when magma or lava cools and solidifies. The mountain of the volcano is made of this cooled and solidified lava. Not all volcanic eruptions are the same, though. Some are more explosive than others. Different types of igneous rock are formed during different eruptions. One factor that affects the type of igneous rock formed by the amount of gas in the magma in the magma chamber. That gas also affects the force of the volcanic eruption. In this activity, you will use a model to investigate what happens during different volcanic eruptions.

GUIDING QUESTION

How can models help us understand what happens during a volcanic eruption?

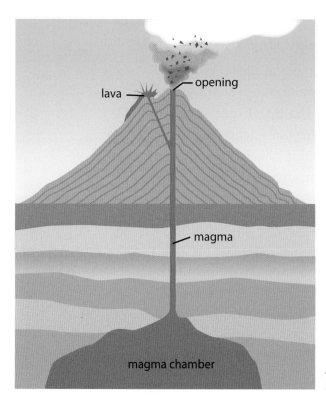

A diagram of the inside of a volcano.

MATERIALS

For each group of four students

- 1 sample of basalt rock
- 1 sample of pumice rock
- 1 vial of baking soda
- 1 bottle of less-gassy "magma" (60-mL; red)
- 1 bottle of more-gassy "magma" (60-mL; colorless)
- 1 cup of water
- 1 plastic volcano model with base
- 1 clear, colorless plastic tube
- 1 rubber stopper
- 1 white plastic scoop
- 1 graduated cup (30-mL)
-   paper towels and/or a sponge

For each pair of students

- 1 magnifying lens

For each student

- 1 pair of chemical splash goggles

SAFETY

Both types of "magma" contain dilute acid. Wear chemical splash goggles, and avoid touching skin and eyes while working with the magma. Wash your hands after completing the activity.

PROCEDURE

Part A: Eruption of Less-Gassy Magma

1. Examine the samples of two types of rock that formed when lava cooled during a volcanic eruption using the magnifying lens. These rocks are called basalt (ba-SALT) and pumice (PUM-is). Compare the two rocks. In your science notebook, make a prediction of which rock you think likely formed from a volcanic eruption with (a) less-gassy magma or (b) more-gassy magma. Explain your reasoning.

2. In your science notebook, make a data table to record your observations of the eruptions with less-gassy magma and more-gassy magma. Be sure to include room in your table to record data for two trials of each eruption.

3. Work with your group to set up your volcano model as shown below by following these steps:

   a. Gently push the clear tube into the mouth of the white volcano cone.

   b. Set the base of the clear tube into the hole of the square plastic tray.

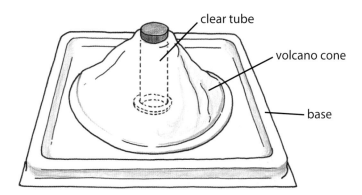

4. Place 1 scoopful of baking soda into the bottom of the volcano tube.

5. Use the graduated cup to measure and pour 5 mL of less-gassy magma into the tube.

6. Without disturbing the model, observe it carefully for 2 min.

7. Record your observations in your science notebook.

8. Rinse your volcano model.

9. Repeat Steps 4–8. Be sure to switch roles among your group members.

Part B: Eruption of More-Gassy Magma

10. Use the graduated cup to measure and pour 2.5 mL of more-gassy magma into the volcano tube.

11. Dip your finger into water, and use it to moisten the bottom of the rubber stopper.

12. Dip the bottom of the stopper into the baking soda so that a thin layer of baking soda sticks to it.

13. Gently cap the volcano tube with the stopper. Trying not to spill any baking soda, insert the stopper snugly into the tube.

14. Quickly turn the entire volcano model upside-down, and then put it back on the table right-side up.

Hint: Balance the volcano model on the palm of one hand. Use the other hand to hold the stopper and tube in place. Turn the model upside-down and right-side up, as shown below. Quickly set the model on the table right-side up.

15. Without disturbing the model, observe it carefully for 2 min.

16. Describe what you observe in your science notebook.

17. Rinse your volcano model.

18. Repeat Steps 10–17. Be sure to switch roles among your group members.

19. Examine the basalt and pumice rock samples again. Look back at the prediction you wrote down in Step 1. With your group of four students, discuss any new ideas you have about which rock more likely formed from a volcanic eruption with (a) less-gassy magma and (b) more-gassy magma. In your science notebook, write down which rock you think formed from less-gassy and which from more-gassy magma. Use evidence from the activity to support your ideas.

ANALYSIS

1. Use your observations of the volcano model to answer the following:

   a. Describe the similarities and differences between the eruptions of volcanoes with less-gassy and more-gassy magma.

   b. Which type of magma produced a more explosive eruption?

2. Imagine a volcano erupting many times over a period of many years. Which of the following landforms is most likely a result of volcanic eruptions: flat plains, a hole or depression, or a mountain? Explain.

3. What were the strengths and weaknesses of the volcano model?

   Hint: Think about ways in which the model did or did not represent real volcanoes or volcanic eruptions.

4. In this activity, you modeled a system. A **system** is a group of interacting objects or processes. Every system includes

   • components: the substances, materials, and processes that make up the system.

   • interactions: the relationships between the substances, materials, and processes in the system.

   • boundaries: the extent of the system, separating those components and processes that are part of the system from those that are not.

   a. In a volcano system, how does the geological process of a volcanic eruption result in the formation of igneous rock?

   b. In a volcano system, how can different volcanic eruptions result in the formation of different kinds of igneous rock?

6

Mapping Locations of Earthquakes and Volcanoes

INVESTIGATION

WHEN CONSIDERING WHERE to store nuclear waste, it is important to know where earthquakes and volcanoes do or may occur. In this activity, you will use technology to plot the locations of major earthquakes and volcanoes using large sets of data. As you analyze and interpret the data, you will look for patterns in the locations of earthquakes and volcanoes.

GUIDING QUESTION

What patterns can we see when examining the locations of earthquakes and volcanoes?

The image on the left shows Mt. Mayon, a volcano in the Philippines. The image on the right shows some of the destruction from the 2017 earthquake in Mexico City.

MATERIALS

For each pair of students

    1 computer with Internet access

For each student

    1 Student Sheet 6.1, "Map of the World"

PROCEDURE

1. Your teacher will assign each pair of students in your group to map a set of either earthquake data or volcano data.

2. On the Internet, go to the *SEPUP Third Edition Geological Processes* page of the SEPUP website at *www.sepuplhs.org/middle/third-edition*, and find the activity named "Mapping Locations of Earthquakes and Volcanoes." From there, select the "Mapping Location Data" link.

3. Follow the onscreen instruction to open the file that you were assigned: earthquakes or volcanoes.

4. Take a few minutes to familiarize yourself with the options in the program. Make sure to try

   • zooming in and out, and moving the map around.

   • changing the colors in the legend at the bottom of the map.

   • highlighting locations on the map.

   • sorting the data by column.

   • switching between Topo View and Ocean View.

   Hint: You can find help through the Help button or by asking your teacher.

5. Look for patterns in the locations of the earthquakes and volcanoes, depending on the data set you have been assigned.

6. In your science notebook, make a T-chart. On the left side, title the column "Patterns and Observations." Title the column on the right "Questions." Using the T-chart, describe the patterns that you see and any questions that you have about the data you are viewing.

7. Use Student Sheet 6.1, "Map of the World," to sketch lines that represent the approximate locations of the volcanoes or earthquakes, if they appear to follow any patterns.

8. Use the program to look for further patterns related to the locations of the 20 strongest earthquakes or the 20 tallest volcanoes, depending on which data set you have been assigned.

9. Start a new row in your T-chart. Using data of strong earthquakes or tall volcanoes, continue to describe the patterns that you see and any questions that you have.

10. Share the map you have drawn on Student Sheet 6.1 with the other pair of students in your group.

11. Discuss any similarities and differences between the earthquake and volcano maps.

12. After viewing the maps of both earthquake and volcano data sets, write down at least two similarities and two differences your group notices. Write down any questions that you have as a group related to the locations of earthquakes and volcanoes.

13. Follow your teacher's directions to discuss your questions and observations with the class.

ANALYSIS

1. Describe any patterns you saw with the locations of earthquakes and volcanoes.

2. After drawing lines to designate the patterns of earthquakes and volcanoes, did you notice any locations that did not seem to be part of any pattern? If so, hypothesize why some earthquakes and/or volcanoes don't appear to fit any pattern.

3. Which parts of the world have had most of the

   a. strongest earthquakes?

   b. tallest volcanoes?

4. If you were to look at the data sets, the earthquake data came with dates included, but the volcano data only provided locations. Why might this be so?

EXTENSION

What are the hazards associated with earthquakes and volcanoes? Visit the *SEPUP Third Edition Geological Processes* page of the SEPUP website at *www.sepuplhs.org/middle/third-edition,* and go to the Natural Hazards link.

7 *Observing Earth's Moving Surface*

INVESTIGATION

IN THE LAST activity, you used technology to determine where there are earthquakes and volcanoes on Earth's surface. But Earth's surface is constantly changing. How can we predict these changes? You may have heard of a phone or car having GPS. You can find GPS in many cellphones, cars, ships, and aircraft; hand-held devices that are used when out hiking or running; and even in wristwatches. **GPS** stands for global positioning system, which refers to a network of satellites around Earth that communicate with GPS receivers located on the ground. Once a ground receiver communicates with at least four satellites, the receiver's location on the ground can be determined.

A person using GPS in a moving car can be instructed to turn left at the next intersection. That is very helpful. But there is a more highly sophisticated GPS used in studying Earth. Using this type of GPS, a particular receiver's position on Earth's surface can be determined with great precision—amazingly, to within a few millimeters (mm). Scientists view thousands of data points a day to track receiver stations' locations to see the amount and direction of ground movement. Since stations are firmly anchored into the ground, the only way the GPS station will move is if the ground to which it is connected moves.

GPS satellites in space and receivers on Earth communicate to determine precise distances between each other.

Geologists study data from GPS stations around the world. Those data help geologists determine how Earth's surface is moving. GPS data recorded over time allow scientists to visualize movements happening far too slowly to observe directly. In this activity, you will analyze and interpret GPS data from a variety of stations. You will determine the direction and speed that Earth's surface is moving.

GUIDING QUESTION

How can GPS data help us understand Earth's surface?

MATERIALS

For each student

3   copies of Student Sheet 7.1, "Analyzing and Interpreting GPS Data"

1   clear metric ruler

PROCEDURE

1. Follow your teacher's directions to complete Student Sheet 7.1, "Analyzing and Interpreting GPS Data," for the GPS station at Hayfork, California, USA.

2. In your group of four, decide which pair of students will analyze the GPS data for Alaska (USA) and who will analyze the data for Iceland.

3. Work with your partner to analyze the data using a fresh copy of Student Sheet 7.1.

4. Share your analysis with the other members of your group.

5. Follow your teacher's directions to complete the analysis of GPS data for the stations in Southern California.

Hayfork, CA

GPS time-series plot for station P332

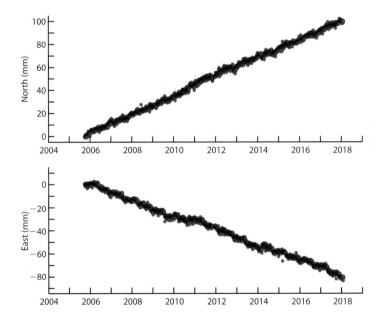

Alaska, USA

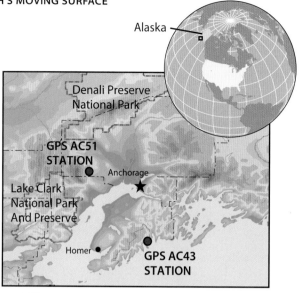

Alaska

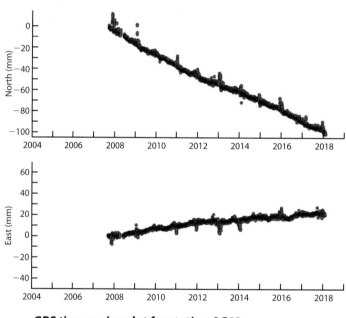

GPS time-series plot for station AC51

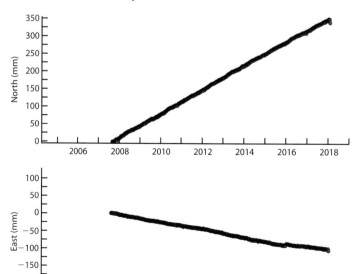

GPS time-series plot for station AC43

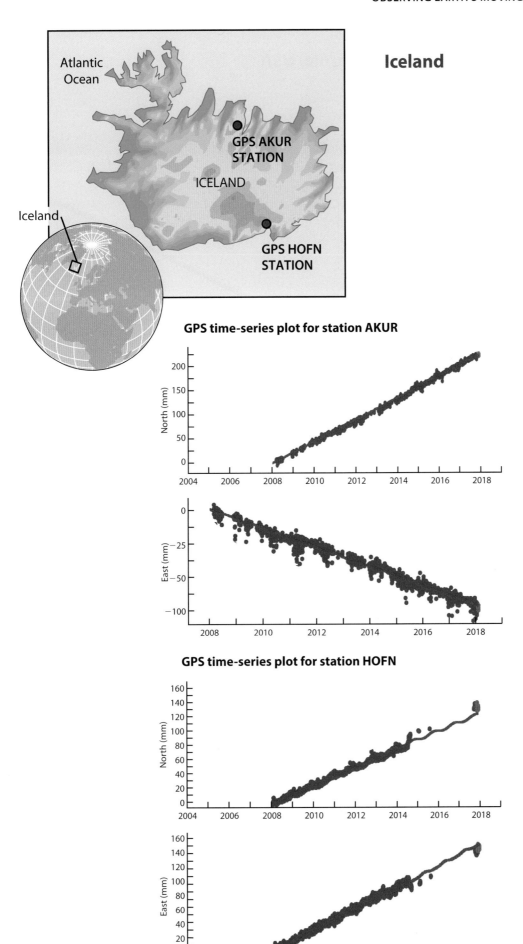

Iceland

GPS time-series plot for station AKUR

GPS time-series plot for station HOFN

Southern California, USA

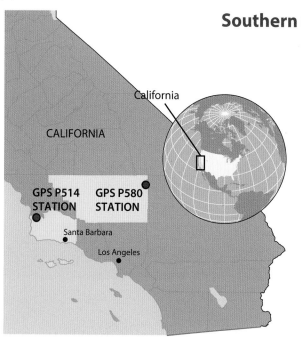

GPS time-series plot for station P514

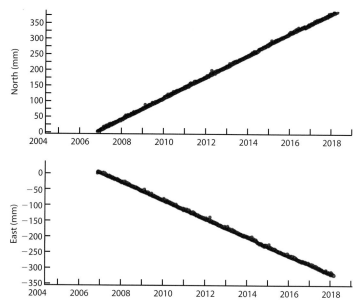

GPS time-series plot for station P580

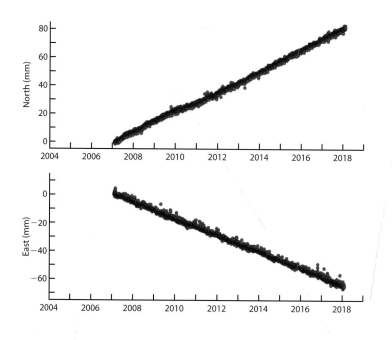

ANALYSIS

1. Here are some time-series plots from a variety of GPS stations. In what overall directions are they moving, and how do you know?

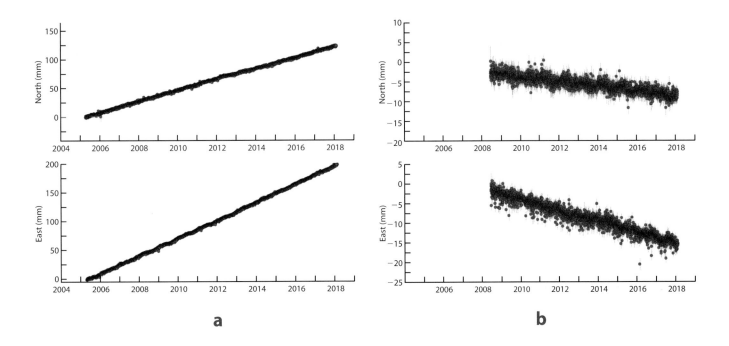

a

b

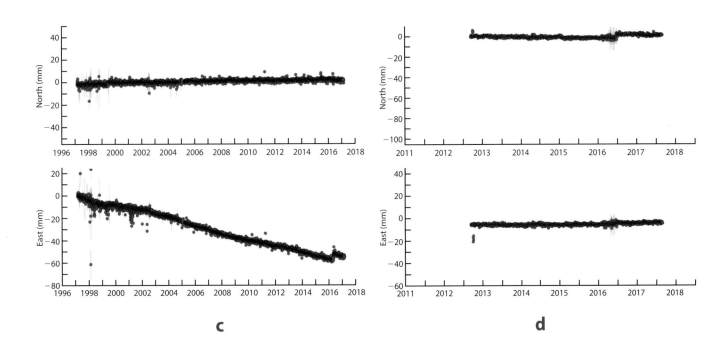

c

d

2. This map shows the location of GPS Station HVWY in Yellowstone National Park, Wyoming, USA. Use the GPS time-series data to describe the overall direction and amount of motion of this station. Note that for this station, the vertical component of the time series has been included to show up–down movement.

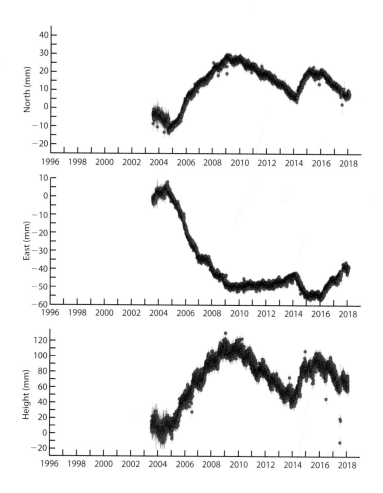

GPS time-series plot for station HVWY

3. Below is an example of a time-series plot that shows a peculiar event. What might have caused this shift to happen? Explain your reasoning.

    Hint: Use your understanding of how to read GPS time series and what you know about Earth's movement to explain what the GPS data show in terms of motion over time.

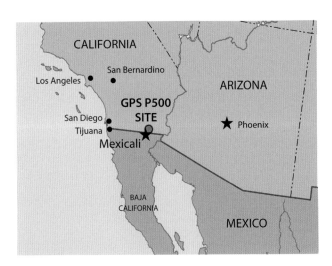

GPS time-series plot for station P500

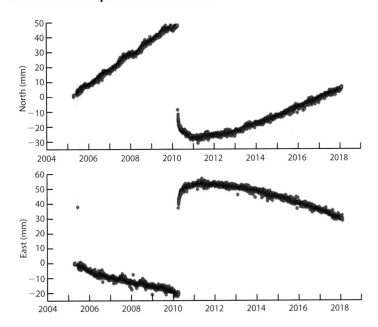

4. The data from the Hayfork, California, GPS station show about 15 mm of northwest motion annually, which might not seem like much. Assuming the rate does not change, how far would that station, and therefore the earth below it, move in the following time periods:

   a. 100 years

   b. 10,000 years

   c. 10,000,000 years

5. Scientists continually look for new ways to learn about their field of study. In your own words, explain how GPS has helped geologists to better understand changes on Earth's surface.

6. How do you think GPS data can be useful for predicting future hazards and deciding where to store nuclear waste? Explain your ideas.

EXTENSION

Visit the *SEPUP Third Edition Geological Processes* page of the SEPUP website at *www.sepuplhs.org/middle/third-edition* to find information about the GPS station nearest you.

8 *Beneath Earth's Surface*

READING

N **"MAPPING LOCATIONS** of Earthquakes and Volcanoes," you learned that earthquakes and volcanoes tend to occur in patterns around the globe. Why do all those earthquakes and volcanoes occur in certain places and not randomly across the planet? To answer these questions, it helps to know more about the structure of the Earth's interior.

GUIDING QUESTION

What is beneath Earth's surface?

Imagine taking a glass elevator to Earth's center. What would you see?

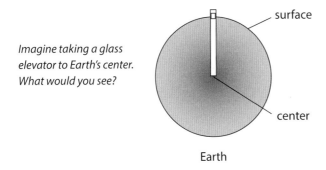

Earth

MATERIALS

For each pair of students

   1 calculator

For each student

   1 Student Sheet 8.1, "Beneath Earth's Surface"

   1 Student Sheet 8.2, "Scaled Drawing of Earth's Interior"

   1 clear metric ruler

PROCEDURE

Follow your teacher's instructions for filling out Student Sheet 8.1 to prepare you for this activity.

READING

Early scientists used evidence from volcanic eruptions to learn about what lies beneath Earth's surface. Over the past 100 years, scientists have learned more about Earth's interior using technology and new methods for gathering data. For example, scientists have learned a lot from analyzing and interpreting data gathered from earthquakes. During an earthquake, energy is transmitted in all directions from the center of the earthquake. The waves that transmit energy as a result of an earthquake are called *seismic waves*. There are different types of seismic waves, and they move through different materials at varying speeds. In general, seismic waves move faster through denser solids than they do through less-dense solids. Not all types of seismic waves can travel through liquids; these different behaviors give scientists clues about the structure of Earth's interior.

Listen as your teacher reads aloud.

Stop when you see this yellow pencil and close your book.

Write down the main ideas you just heard.

Scientists use seismometers to measure the seismic waves transmitted from earthquakes. By analyzing and comparing seismic-wave data from many earthquakes, scientists have been able to determine the state—solid or liquid—and the properties of materials that make up Earth's interior.

Scientists have used seismic-wave data and other evidence to explain that Earth has three main layers: a crust, a mantle, and a core. Information about each of these layers of Earth is presented in the table below:

LAYERS OF EARTH	APPROXIMATE DEPTH BELOW SURFACE (km)	STATE	MATERIAL	TEMPERATURE (°C)
Crust	5–40 on average	Solid	Many kinds of rocks	0–700
Mantle	40–2,800	Mostly solid. (Varies with temperature and pressure.)	Iron, magnesium, and silicate compounds	700–2,800
Outer Core	2,800–5,200	Liquid	Iron and nickel	2,800–6,000
Inner Core	5,200–6,400	Solid	Iron and nickel	Over 6,000

The crust is the outermost layer of the Earth. Below Earth's crust is the mantle. The mantle is almost 3,000 km thick, which is about the same as the distance from New York City to Denver, Colorado. Just as the land from New York to Colorado is not all the same, neither is the mantle. The uppermost part of the mantle is relatively cold compared with what is below it. Thus, it remains in a hard, solid state. Because the upper mantle and the crust are solid, geologists refer to the combination of these hard, solid layers as the **lithosphere** (*litho* means "stone" in Greek).

The lithosphere is approximately 100 km thick, on average. Earth's lithosphere is broken into pieces of various sizes called **lithospheric plates**, also referred to as Earth's plates. Places on the surface where two or more of Earth's plates meet are called **plate boundaries**. At plate boundaries, plates can move toward each other, move away from each other, or slide past each other. Volcanoes and earthquakes commonly appear on or near plate boundaries and are related to that motion.

Just below the lithosphere, between the depths of 100 km and about 250 km, lies a layer of the mantle called the **asthenosphere** (ah-STHEEN-o-sfeer) (from Greek, where *a*- means "without," and *stheno*- means "strength"). The asthenosphere is a layer of solid rock that can flow and change shape. This weak, soft layer beneath the harder lithosphere allows the lithospheric plates to continuously move around very slowly. The movement of the lithospheric plates and their interactions at plate boundaries leads to the pattern of earthquakes and volcanoes on Earth's surface.

Geologist installing seismometers to measure seismic waves from earthquakes

Map of Earth's Lithospheric Plates

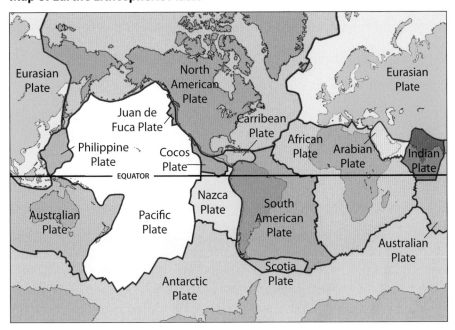

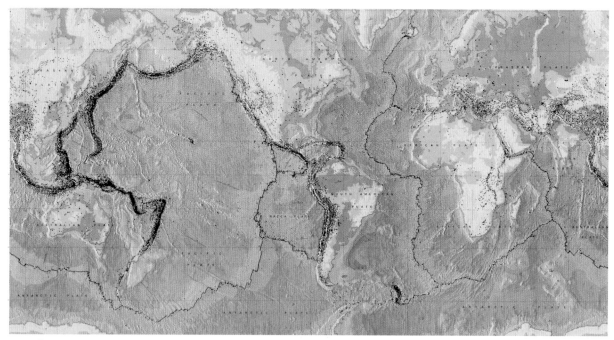

Map of recent earthquakes and existing volcanoes on Earth. Black dots mark the locations of individual earthquakes and volcanoes.

One way that geologists study and monitor lithospheric plate movement is by using GPS technology. Data from GPS stations fixed in the lithosphere indicate the general direction Earth's plates are moving as they shift on top of weak, soft asthenosphere. The GPS data represented on the map below shows the direction and rate of plate movement in the western United States.

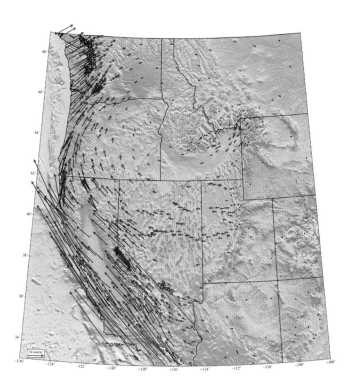

ANALYSIS

1. Which layer or layers of Earth

    a. are the hottest?

    b. are at Earth's center?

    c. are completely solid?

    d. contain the asthenosphere?

2. Copy the five words and phrases shown below:

    outer core

    lithosphere

    upper mantle

    solid

    crust

    a. Look for a relationship among the words. Cross out the word or phrase that does not belong.

    b. Circle the word or phrase that includes all the other words.

    c. Explain how the word or phrase you circled is related to the other words in the list.

    Your teacher will give you Student Sheet 8.2, "Scaled Drawing of Earth's Interior." Use it and the information from the reading to answer Analysis items 3 and 4.

3. On Student Sheet 8.2, answer Parts a–g to create a scaled drawing of Earth's layers. If you have colored pencils available, you may want to color in the different layers.

    a. Record the distance in kilometers from Earth's surface to its center.

    b. To make an accurate drawing, you first need to determine the scale, which tells how many kilometers each centimeter on your drawing will represent. On Student Sheet 8.2, use a clear metric ruler to measure and record the distance from the circle, representing Earth's surface, to its center in centimeters. Measure to the nearest 0.1 cm, and record this measurement in the table.

    c. Calculate the scale by dividing the actual distance to the center of Earth in kilometers by the distance you measured in centimeters on the drawing. Record your scale in the table.

   d. In the table on Student Sheet 8.2, record the lowest depth
      of each Earth layer in kilometers. Then, use your scale and a
      calculator to determine the scaled depth of each location in
      centimeters.

   e. Use the ruler to measure the depth of each layer from Earth's
      surface.
      Hint: Save the crust–mantle boundary for last.

   f. Label each layer with its name, state of matter, and tempera-
      ture. If you don't have room to record the data on the drawing,
      write it next to the drawing, draw a box around the data, and
      draw an arrow to point from the box to the appropriate layer.

   g. Calculate the scaled depths of the lithosphere and the asthe-
      nosphere. Draw one dotted line on your diagram to indicate
      the lower boundary of the lithosphere and another dotted line
      to indicate the lower boundary of the asthenosphere. Label
      the lithosphere and asthenosphere. Write the state of matter
      of each layer.

4. Scientists recommend storing nuclear waste deep underground.
   Use the model you created on Student Sheet 8.2 and the information about each layer to predict the best depth in Earth's interior
   for nuclear waste storage.

   a. In which layer of Earth do you think nuclear waste should be
      stored?

   b. Place an "X" on that layer on your copy of Student Sheet 8.2.

   c. Explain your reasoning for the prediction you made.

   d. How does the "X" you put on Student Sheet 8.2 compare with
      your initial thinking on Student Sheet 8.1?

EXTENSION 1

To learn more about how seismic waves interact with the layers of
Earth, visit the *SEPUP Third Edition Geological Processes* page of the
SEPUP website at *www.sepuplhs.org/middle/third-edition* for links with
further information about the different types of waves and how they
help scientists learn about Earth's interior. Be sure to check out the
Animations tab.

EXTENSION 2

New discoveries can change our thinking. Learn about Inge Lehmann, an important geologist who used seismic-wave data to figure out that Earth's inner core is solid. Visit the *SEPUP Third Edition Geological Processes* page of the SEPUP website at *www. sepuplhs.org/middle/third-edition* for links with further information about her story.

9 *Modeling Earthquakes*

MODELING

WHY DO EARTHQUAKES occur at plate boundaries? In this activity, you will use common materials to model what happens when Earth's plates move. As you use the model, you will investigate how forces between moving plates cause earthquakes. You will plan and carry out your own investigation to determine what factors influence the **magnitude** or size of an earthquake. Strong earthquakes can cause problems for the safe storage of nuclear waste, so it is important to understand how and why earthquakes happen when deciding where to store nuclear waste.

GUIDING QUESTION

How can models help us understand earthquakes?

Collapsed building in Concepción, Chile, after a very large earthquake happened in February, 2010

MATERIALS

For each group of four students

  1 long strip of sandpaper

  1 block of wood, with coarse sandpaper and hook attached

  1 block of wood, with fine sandpaper and hook attached

  1 tape measure

     rubber bands, thick

     rubber bands, thin

     masking tape

PROCEDURE

Part A: Setting Up and Testing the Model

1. Tape the long strip of sandpaper to a flat surface so it is stretched out flat.

2. Place one of the wooden blocks on the end of the sandpaper strip so the hook is pointing along the sandpaper strip. Make sure the face of the block covered with sandpaper is in full contact with the sandpaper strip.

3. Fasten the tape measure alongside the strip of sandpaper so that the zero mark on the tape is in line with the front edge of the block with the hook.

4. Loop one of the rubber bands onto the hook, and pull slowly and steadily. Do not use a jerky or sudden motion.

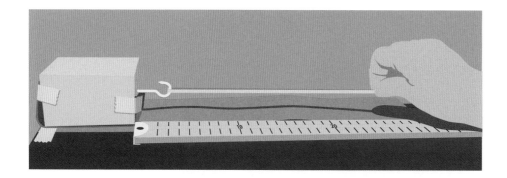

5. Pull steadily until the block moves. Stop pulling as soon as the block moves, and use the markings on the tape measure to make note of the location of the hand of the person who was pulling. Record this position in your science notebook.

6. Measure the distance the block moved, and record it in your science notebook, as well as your observations of how the model moved.

7. Repeat Steps 2–6 two more times to see how consistent your results are. Record your results each time.

Part B: Planning and Carrying Out an Investigation

8. With your group, brainstorm at least three possible variables to test that may change the movement of the block.

9. As a group, choose a variable to test.

10. Design an experiment that will determine how changing your variable will affect the behavior of the model.

    When designing your experiment, think about these questions:

    - What is the purpose of your experiment?

    - What variable are you testing?

    - What variables will you keep the same?

    - What is your hypothesis?

    - What is your control?

    - How many trials will you conduct?

    - Will you collect qualitative or quantitative data, or both? How will the data help you form a conclusion?

    - How will you record the data?

11. Record your hypothesis and your planned procedure in your science notebook.

12. Obtain your teacher's approval of your experiment.

13. Make a data table that has space for all the data you need to record during the experiment.

14. Conduct your investigation, and record your results.

15. Be prepared to share the results of your experiment with the class.

ANALYSIS

1. In science, we use models to help us understand phenomena, but all models have strengths and weaknesses.

   a. What are the strengths of this model? Explain your reasoning.

   b. What are the weaknesses of this model? Explain your reasoning.

   c. Come up with at least one idea to improve the model used in this activity. Explain how your idea would improve the model.

2. In Part B, how did changing your variable affect the movement of the block in the earthquake model? Use data you collected as evidence to support your claim.

3. Revisit the hypothesis and experimental design you wrote for Part B.

   a. Did the data you collected support your hypothesis?

   b. Did you collect enough high-quality data to answer your question? What is one way in which you could improve your experimental design to collect higher-quality data?

4. After listening to your classmates share the results of their experiments for Part B, which variable affected the movement of the block in the earthquake model the most? Why do you think that is?

5. Use the model to explain how earthquakes happen.

6. What additional questions do you have about how or why earthquakes happen after working with the earthquake model?

7. Some geological processes that cause changes to Earth's surface happen suddenly, and others happen slowly. Describe one sudden change and one slow change using evidence from this activity.

EXTENSION

All earthquakes occur along faults. *Faults* are areas of weakness in Earth's crust often found on or near plate boundaries. The rock along either side of a fault moves at different rates or in different directions, causing earthquakes. One well-known fault system is the San Andreas fault, at the boundary between the Pacific and North American plates. Other examples include the Northridge and Hayward Fault Systems. Visit the *SEPUP Third Edition Geological Processes* page of the SEPUP website at *www.sepuplhs.org/middle/third-edition* for links to learn more about earthquakes and faults.

10 | *Plate Boundaries*

COMPUTER SIMULATION

FROM GPS DATA, we know that Earth's lithospheric plates move very slowly—even the fastest plates move less than 10 cm per year. But they have also been moving for millions of years. Over long periods of time, the plates can move great distances and cause many changes to Earth's surface. At plate boundaries, Earth's plates can spread apart, move towards each other, move past each other, or some combination of these. In this activity, you will investigate what happens to Earth's surface at different types of plate boundaries.

GUIDING QUESTION

What happens where Earth's plates meet?

The Red Sea was formed by spreading between the African and Arabian plates.

MATERIALS

For each student

    1   Student Sheet 10.1, "Spreading Plate Observations"

    1   Student Sheet 10.2, "Other Plate Movement"

PROCEDURE

Part A: Spreading Plates

Visit the *SEPUP Third Edition Geological Processes* page of the SEPUP website at *www.sepuplhs.org/middle/third-edition,* and go to the Plate Motion Simulation.

1. Set the direction for Plate 1 to move by clicking on the arrow pointing left ($\leftarrow$).

2. On Student Sheet 10.1, "Spreading Plate Observations," record the directions in which Plate 1 and Plate 2 will move.

3. Click on the SEE PLATES OVER TIME button at the bottom of the screen. You should now see a legend on the bottom left of the screen. Read the legend so you know what each symbol means.

4. Write the scientific term for this plate boundary type, seen in the upper left corner, on your Student Sheet.

5. Use the PICK TIME button to set the simulation to run for 10 years.

6. Click on the RUN button to begin the simulation, and carefully observe what happens.

7. Record your observations on Student Sheet 10.1.

8. Reset the screen by clicking on the RESET TIME button.

9. Repeat Steps 4–8, but run your simulation for 100 years.

10. Repeat Steps 4–8, but run your simulation for 1,000 years.

11. Repeat Steps 4–8, but run your simulation for 1 million years.

12. Repeat Steps 4–8, but run your simulation for 5 million years.

13. Repeat Steps 4–8, but run your simulation for 20 million years.

Part B: Other Types of Plate Motion

14. Reset the simulation by clicking the HOME button.

15. Choose a different direction for Plate 1 to move.

    Hint: do not click on the arrow pointing left (←) again or you will repeat your observation of a spreading plate boundary).

16. On Student Sheet 10.2, "Other Plate Movement," circle the directions in which Plate 1 and Plate 2 will move, and record the scientific term for the boundary type that you are investigating on your Student Sheet.

17. Click on the SEE PLATES OVER TIME button. If you are investigating a plate boundary where plates collide, record the type of lithosphere (continental or oceanic) on the same line of Student Sheet 10.1 as the type of boundary.

18. Use the PICK TIME button to set the simulation to run for 20 million years.

19. Click on the RUN button, and observe what happens. Repeat the simulation with different combinations of lithosphere, or run it for different periods of time so you can make better observations.

20. Record your observations on Student Sheet 10.1.

21. If you selected a plate boundary where plates collide, click on the button labeled WHAT IF TWO OCEANIC PLATES COLLIDE? and repeat Steps 16–18. If you did not select a convergent boundary, go on to the next step.

22. Reset the simulation by clicking the HOME button.

23. Repeat Steps 14–21, but select a new direction for Plate 1 to move.

ANALYSIS

1. In the simulation, how many years passed before major changes to Earth's surface were noticeable?

2. Why do the geological processes that occur at convergent boundaries vary?

3. In your science notebook, make a table like the one below. Identify the scientific term for each type of plate boundary, and then place an "X" to identify what is likely to happen at each type of plate boundary. Describe the patterns you observed in the data.

Comparing Plate Motion

Types of plate motion	Scientific term for boundary type	What might happen at this type of boundary?			
		Earthquakes	Volcanoes	Mountain forming	Trench
Moving towards each other					
Spreading apart					
Moving past one another					

4. Do you think Earth's continents and oceans will look the same in the future as they do now? Why or why not? Use evidence from the activity to support your ideas.

5. **Reflection:** Earth's plates are constantly moving, yet Earth's surface looks relatively the same each day. Why don't we observe changes to Earth's surface every day?

11 *Understanding Plate Boundaries*

READING

MANY OF THE world's most active volcanoes are located around the edges of the Pacific Ocean. People refer to this area as the "Ring of Fire," shown in the map below. About 90% of the world's earthquakes also occur in this region. These geological processes are caused by interactions between the plates at the plate boundaries that surround the Ring of Fire. Why do so many volcanoes and earthquakes happen at plate boundaries?

GUIDING QUESTION

How can our understanding of geological processes at plate boundaries allow us to predict and prepare for natural hazards?

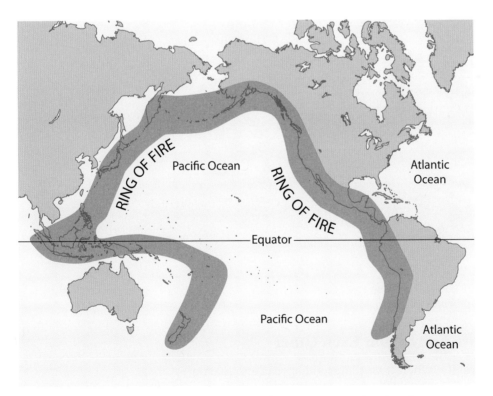

Map showing the Ring of Fire, an area with frequent volcanic eruptions and earthquakes

MATERIALS

For each student

1   Student Sheet 11.1, "Directed Reading Table: Understanding Plate Boundaries"

PROCEDURE

1. Read the article with a partner.

2. After you read each section, use evidence from the text to complete Student Sheet 11.1 for that plate boundary.

READING

Earth's lithosphere is broken into plates that are in constant motion. The plates may be moving apart, or moving towards each other, or moving past each other. Over geological time, important geological processes—such as the formation of mountain ranges, earthquakes, and volcanoes—take place along the boundaries where lithospheric plates meet.

Types of Plate Boundaries

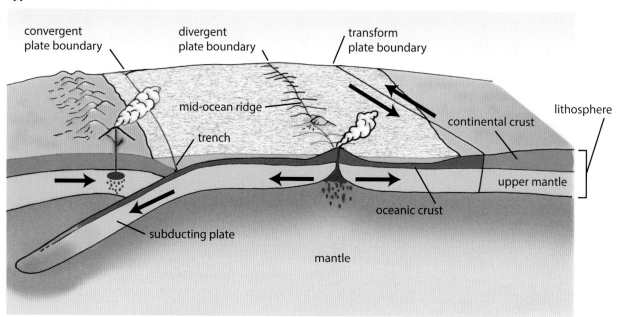

Plates That Move Away From Each Other

Geologists call a region where two plates are spreading apart a **divergent** (dy-VER-junt) **plate boundary.** Volcanoes as well as earthquakes are common along divergent plate boundaries. As the plates move apart, the lithosphere thins and lava erupts onto the surface.

New lithosphere forms as the lava cools and solidifies to form igneous rock. (See the figure on the previous page.)

Often, divergent plate boundaries are under the ocean. Large underwater volcanic mountain chains that form along divergent plate boundaries are called **mid-ocean ridges.** One of the largest mid-ocean ridges is the Mid-Atlantic Ridge. This ridge is between the North American and Eurasian plates in the middle of the Atlantic Ocean.

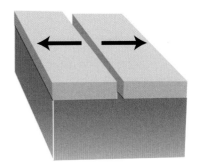

Plates moving away from each other

When the plates move away from each other at divergent plate boundaries, a rift valley forms. A rift valley is a long depression between mountains that forms due to spreading plate movement. In rift valleys where there is active plate movement, earthquakes and volcanoes are common. In 2005, a large earthquake happened near Lake Tanganyika in Africa. This earthquake was caused by divergent plate motion where two sections of the African plate are moving away from each other.

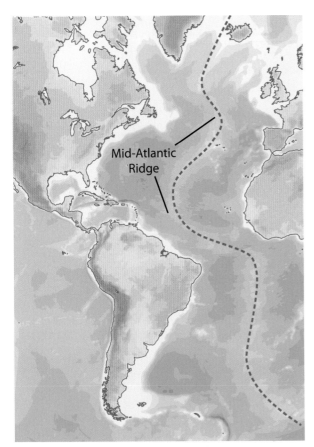

The Mid-Atlantic Ridge stretches from the Arctic Ocean to the Southern Ocean.

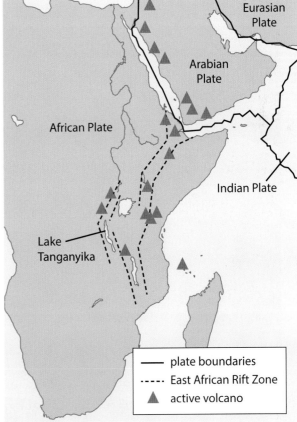

The East African Rift Zone is a region where sections of the African Plate are moving away from each other.

Plates That Move Toward Each Other

Geologists call a region where two plates are moving towards each other a **convergent** (kun-VER-junt) **plate boundary.** The geological processes that happen along a convergent plate boundary depend on the type of lithosphere at the edge of the colliding plates. Earth's lithosphere—which includes the crust and solid upper mantle—varies in thickness and density over Earth's surface. The crust that makes up the oceans is generally thinner than the crust that makes up the continents. Oceanic crust is usually about 10 km thick. Continental crust ranges from 20 to 80 km thick. For this reason, the lithosphere is about 100–150 km thick under the ocean and up to 300 km thick below some continents. Despite being thinner, oceanic lithosphere is denser than continental lithosphere because its crust is made up of denser rock, primarily basalt.

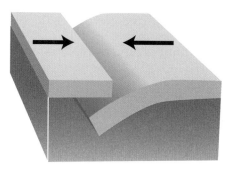

Plates moving toward each other

Subduction formed the Villarrica Volcano, a large stratovolcano in Chile.

When two plates move towards each other, the denser plate sinks below the less-dense plate. When continental and oceanic lithosphere move towards each other, the denser oceanic lithosphere sinks into the mantle and is destroyed. The same process also happens when two oceanic lithospheric plates move towards each other – the denser plate sinks beneath the less dense plate. The process of one plate being pulled below another plate is known as **subduction** (sub-DUK-shun). Subduction forms a **trench** along the plate boundary. A trench is a deep, narrow depression on the sea floor. At a convergent plate boundary where subduction is occurring, volcanoes form on the surface of the overlying lithospheric plate. The volcanoes that form at convergent plate boundaries where continental and oceanic lithosphere move toward each other are typically *stratovolcanoes*—large volcanoes that erupt violently as a result of more-gassy magma.

The volcanic mountains along the western coast of South America formed by subduction. Oceanic lithosphere of the Pacific plate subducted below continental lithosphere of the South American plate. Subduction formed the Peru–Chile trench on the ocean floor along this boundary. Subduction is also happening in the Pacific Northwest of the United States. Oceanic lithosphere of the Juan de Fuca plate is being pulled under continental lithosphere of the North American plate.

When two plates of continental lithosphere move towards each other, they tend to crumple and are pushed upward. This motion can form very tall mountains and cause earthquakes. The Himalayan mountains formed when continental lithosphere on the Indian Plate met continental lithosphere on the Eurasian plate. Several of the world's highest mountains, including Mt. Everest, are part of the Himalayas and were formed in this collision.

Plates That Move Past Each Other

Geologists call the region where two plates move past each other a **transform plate boundary**. Here, lithosphere is neither created nor destroyed. Earthquakes are common as the plates move past one another.

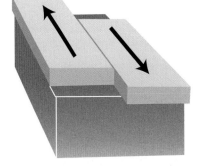

Plates moving past each other

A transform plate boundary exists along the western edge of California. The boundary is between part of the Pacific plate and part of the North American plate. Plate motion causes many earthquakes along this boundary. Two powerful earthquakes happened along this boundary near San Francisco in 1906 and 1989. These earthquakes each lasted less than 1 min. But the ground-shaking and related natural hazards caused heavy damage to the city.

Damage to buildings in San Francisco after the 1906 Earthquake and the fires that followed

Damage to buildings in San Francisco after the 1989 Earthquake

Volcanoes and Plates

Most earthquakes and volcanoes occur along plate boundaries. But sometimes they form elsewhere. For example, volcanoes formed each of the Hawaiian Islands. Lava from eruptions over hundreds of thousands of years built up the islands. Yet the Hawaiian Islands are located far from any plate boundaries. Hawaii, the large island at the southeastern end of the island chain, is the only one of those islands that still has an active volcano.

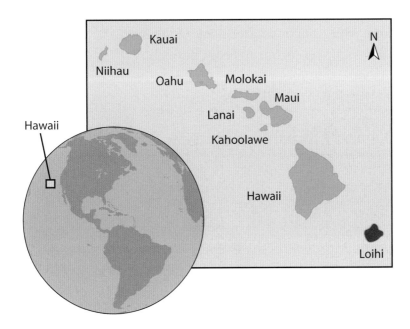

The volcanoes that formed the islands are called *shield volcanoes*. They are typically large and broad in shape. These volcanoes release swift-moving lava. Because of the less-gassy magma, these volcanoes tend to have less explosive eruptions than other types of volcanoes. People can often safely walk near these erupting volcanoes.

A geologist uses a radar gun to measure how fast the lava is moving during an eruption on the Big Island of Hawaii.

A new island called Loihi [low-EE-Hee] has begun to form beneath the ocean southeast of the island of Hawaii. But don't start making vacation plans to visit Loihi just yet. Scientists predict it will rise above the ocean's surface in about 1 million years.

One argument about how the Hawaiian island chain formed suggests that molten material in a region called a *hot spot* rose to the surface from the deep mantle. According to this argument, movement of the Pacific plate carried each of the islands toward the northwest, away from the hot spot. Other arguments are based on the properties of plates. For example, volcanoes might form when thin or cracked areas of the lithosphere allow hot material from the upper mantle to break through.

The 2011 Earthquake and Fukushima Nuclear Accident in Japan

On March 11, 2011, a huge earthquake rocked Japan. This strong earthquake originated 70 km (43 miles) off the coast of the largest Japanese island, Honshu. This earthquake resulted from a nearby convergent plate boundary where the oceanic Pacific plate was subducting beneath a continental plate. The movement of the sea floor during the earthquake generated a large *tsunami* (tsoo-NAH-mee). A tsunami is a large wave that forms when an earthquake, volcano, landslide, or other event moves a large amount of water. The tsunami hit the coast of Japan soon after the earthquake. At its highest, the wave from the earthquake reached 38 m (125 feet).

The tsunami killed more than 15,000 people and injured over 5,000. It destroyed over 330,000 structures, including buildings, roads, bridges, and railways. The cost of the earthquake and tsunami damage has been estimated at hundreds of billions of U.S. dollars.

The earthquake and resulting tsunami led to a serious accident at a nuclear power plant. The reactor was built to withstand the ground-shaking and it did. However, the seawater from the tsunami caused problems with the electrical power and the back-up generator, which caused the cooling system to fail at three of the six nuclear reactors at the Fukushima Daiichi

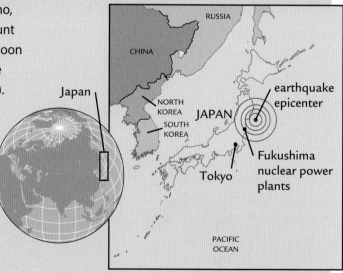

power plant on Honshu. The reactors overheated, causing a nuclear fuel meltdown and explosions. Several workers died, and more were exposed to radiation. This incident released radioactive material into the air and water surrounding the plant. The long-term effects of the radiation released to the environment are not yet known. The greatest fear is that exposure to radiation will lead to increased deaths from cancer.

Although nuclear waste does not explode, the accident in Japan has increased concern in the United States and elsewhere about all aspects of nuclear safety.

A damaged building at the Fukushima Daiichi nuclear power plant 1 year after the earthquake and tsunami

ANALYSIS

1. Describe two ways in which the movement of lithospheric plates can result in the formation of mountains.

2. Trenches form at convergent plate boundaries, whereas mid-ocean ridges form at divergent plate boundaries. How are these land-forms similar and different?

3. Should nuclear waste be stored deep underground near plate boundaries? Explain your ideas using evidence from this activity.

12 *The Continent Puzzle*

INVESTIGATION

YOU HAVE LEARNED the different ways that lithospheric plates move. But how have the geological processes caused by plate movement changed Earth's surface over time? How do we know what ancient Earth looked like? Modern humans have been around for only hundreds of thousands of years, or 0.01% of Earth's 4.6-billion-year history.

Scientists use evidence from rock and fossils to figure out when events happened in Earth's history. Scientists use this evidence to put the major events in Earth's history in order. They usually refer to time periods of thousands, millions, and billions of years as **geological time**.

Alfred Wegener (1880-1930) was a German scientist. Over many years, he gathered evidence to support a new idea about Earth's history over geological time. His evidence included the location of fossils and rock layers on different continents. In this activity, you will use a model to analyze some of Wegener's evidence to better understand his idea.

GUIDING QUESTION

What evidence can we use to help us understand the movement of Earth's plates over time?

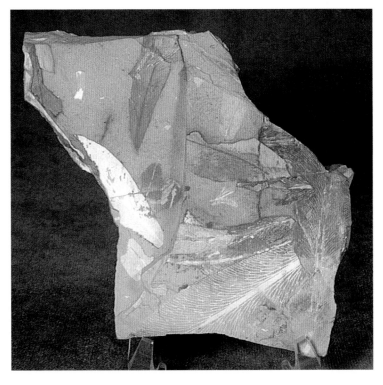

Fossilized Glossopteris leaves

MATERIALS

For each group of four students

    1 set of 7 World Puzzle pieces

    1 set of markers or colored pencils

For each student

    1 Student Sheet 12.1, "World Puzzle"

    1 Student Sheet 12.2, "Earth's Surface Through Geological Time"

PROCEDURE

Part A: World Puzzle

1. With your group, carefully examine the location of the world's continents on the map below.

2. Record the names of the six continents in your science notebook.

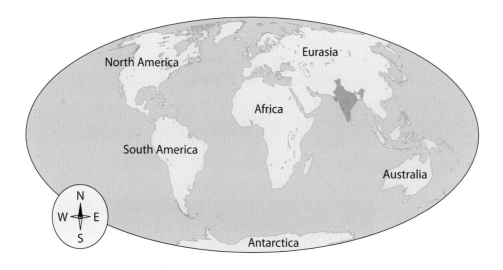

The country of India can be seen in orange on the Eurasian continent.

3. Compare each World Puzzle piece to the continents on the map. Put a star next to each continent in your list that is represented by a puzzle piece. Then record the name(s) of any additional pieces.

4. Work with your group to arrange your puzzle pieces in locations similar to the ones shown on the world map.

5. Look at the symbols on some of the pieces. The symbols represent types of fossils or rocks found in several locations. Read the key to these symbols, which is shown below.

Key to Symbols on World Puzzle

 Glossopteris, an extinct fern-like plant that could grow to 3.7 meters (12 feet) in height

 Mesosaurus (MESS-oh-saw-rus), an extinct freshwater reptile about 0.5 meters (1.5 feet) in length

 Cynognathus (sy-nog-NAY-thus), an extinct land reptile about the size of a wolf

 Lystrosaurus (liss-tro-SAW-rus), an extinct land reptile about 1 meter (3 feet) long

---

6. Using evidence from the symbols on the puzzle pieces, work with your group to try to place all of the pieces into a single shape. Work together to decide where each piece belongs.

    Remember to listen to and consider the explanations and ideas of the other members of your group. If you disagree with other members of your group, explain why you disagree.

7. Once your group has agreed on your puzzle, ask your teacher for Student Sheet 12.1, "World Puzzle." Use solid black lines to sketch the shapes of the puzzle pieces. Label the individual puzzle pieces with current continent names in your sketch.

8. Use five different-colored markers or different symbols to label the boxes in the key on the bottom of Student Sheet 12.1. Using the colors or symbols from your key, mark the locations of the fossil and rock evidence in your sketch of the completed World Puzzle.

9. Move the pieces back into positions similar to the location of the continents today. Then slowly move the pieces back together into the single shape.

10. Discuss with your group what this puzzle might tell you about the history of Earth.

Part B: The History of Earth's Surface

11. Ask your teacher for a copy of Student Sheet 12.2, "Earth's Surface Through Geological Time."

12. Discuss with your group what you think has happened to the land on the surface of Earth during geological time.

13. Compare the outline you sketched on Student Sheet 12.1 with Student Sheet 12.1. Identify when in Earth's history the continents were arranged in a similar way. Record this time period and the name of the land at this time on Student Sheet 12.1.

ANALYSIS

1. There are six continents and there were seven puzzle pieces. One of the puzzle pieces was different from the others in that it did not represent a continent. Why do you think this difference was part of the model?

   Hint: Think about how you used the puzzle pieces to model changes on Earth's surface.

2. Explain how Earth's surface has changed over geological time.

   a. Describe what has happened to the land on Earth's surface over the past 425 million years.

   b. What types of evidence did the puzzle provide about changes on Earth's surface? Choose two pieces of evidence from the model. For each, describe what it is and how it supports the theory that the position of the continents has changed over geological time.

   Hint: Think about how you used the puzzle pieces to model changes on Earth's surface.

3. A friend says that changes to Earth's surface happen only very suddenly, like when the ground shakes during an earthquake or when a volcano erupts. Do you agree or disagree with your friend? Use evidence to support your position and explain your reasoning.

4. Alfred Wegener used the phrase **continental** (kon-ti-NEN-tul) **drift** for his idea that the continents were once joined together as a single large continent and then slowly moved great distances apart. Why do you think Wegener used different pieces of evidence to support continental drift? Explain your ideas.

5. In the activity "Storing Nuclear Waste," you learned that nuclear waste can be dangerous for at least 250,000 years. How would you compare that amount of time to the time gone by since the supercontinent Pangea existed? How would you compare it to the age of Earth?

   Hint: Use fractions, percentages, or ratios to describe the relationship.

EXTENSION

Visit the *SEPUP Third Edition Geological Processes* page of the SEPUP website at *www.sepuplhs.org/middle/third-edition* to learn what scientists predict about future plate movements. How will Earth's surface be different in the future?

13 *The Theory of Plate Tectonics*

I N THE LAST activity, you used Alfred Wegener's evidence to investigate the movement of Earth's continents over geological time. Today, geologists know that continents are not all that moves—entire lithospheric plates move. The theory that the lithospheric plates are in constant motion is called **plate tectonics** (tek-TAWN-iks). But what new evidence led to the theory of plate tectonics?

GUIDING QUESTION

How did Wegener's idea of continental drift lead to the theory of plate tectonics?

MATERIALS

For each student

1   Student Sheet 13.1, "Plate Tectonics Video"

At mid-ocean ridges, lava erupts from volcanoes, then cools and solidifies to form mounds of igneous rock called pillow lavas.

PROCEDURE

1. Watch the video segments on continental drift and plate tectonics.

2. Answer as many questions on Student Sheet 13.1, "Plate Tectonics Video," as you can.

3. Watch the video segments again.

4. Complete Student Sheet 13.1.

ANALYSIS

1. Why were scientists surprised to find coal in the Arctic?

2. The idea of continental drift eventually led to the modern theory of plate tectonics. To help you remember similarities and differences between these two ideas, create a larger version of the table shown below in your science notebook.

   a. Compare continental drift and plate tectonics by recording unique features of each idea in the column with that label.

      Hint: Think about what you have learned about these ideas in the last two activities.

   b. Record features that are common to both of these ideas in the column labeled "Both."

Continental Drift	Both	Plate Tectonics

3. Imagine that you are writing an article about what you are learning in science class for your school newspaper. In your own words, explain

   • the theory of plate tectonics.

   • how earthquakes, volcanoes, and mountain formation are related to plate tectonics.

• how changes to Earth's surface caused by plate motion can be gradual or sudden, and whether they affect small or large areas of Earth. Explain how scientists know these changes have happened both today and in the past.

Be as specific as you can, and include evidence.

4. Below you will find a map that shows the age of the oceanic lithosphere on the sea floor.

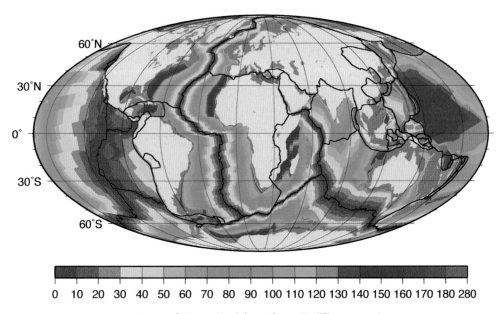

Age of Oceanic Lithosphere (million years)

a. Describe the patterns you see on the map. What happens to the age of the lithosphere as you move further from the mid-ocean ridge?

b. How do the patterns in the map relate to your observations from the video?

c. Look back at Student Sheet 12.1, "World Puzzle." How would you explain the evidence both in the map below and from Student Sheet 12.1?

5. What surprised or impressed you about Alfred Wegener and his approach to science?

14 What Makes the Plates Move?

MODELING

CONVINCING EVIDENCE SHOWS that Earth's lithospheric plates are constantly moving. There are two main forces that drives plate motion: gravity and convection.

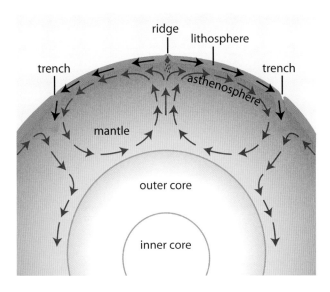

Red arrows represent the movement of the mantle due to convection. Black arrows represent the movement of the plates due to gravity.

The primary force is gravity. **Gravity** is a force that pulls objects towards each other. At divergent plate boundaries, the volcanic land-forms that make up mid-ocean ridges rise to around 2,000 m above the sea floor. This height causes plates on either side of the ridge to move down the slope, away from the mid-ocean ridge due to gravity.

When an oceanic plate collides with another plate at a convergent plate boundary, one sinks into the mantle to form a trench. As the edge of the oceanic plate subducts the other plate, gravity pulls the rest of the plate down with it. The whole plate is pulled toward Earth's center. Scientists call this downward movement of the plate due to gravity *slab pull*. The movement of the plates due to slab pull is represented by black arrows in the diagram above.

Another force that acts on plates is thermal energy from Earth's hot interior. You learned that the core is the hottest layer of Earth. It is hotter than the mantle and so transfers thermal energy to the mantle. **Thermal energy** is the internal energy of a substance due to the movement of particles within the substance.

Scientists think that this transfer of thermal energy from core to mantle causes convection in the mantle. **Convection** is the transfer of thermal energy by the movement of matter of different temperatures. Convection in the mantle, shown in red arrows in the diagram above, is a driver of plate movement. While we often think about convection occurring in liquids, like boiling water, convection can also occur in solids, like Earth's mantle.

In this activity, you will investigate how both convection and gravity work by using models. The models will help you learn about how temperature differences can cause substances, like mantle material, to move and how gravity affects the movement of Earth's plates.

GUIDING QUESTION

What drives plate motion?

MATERIALS

For the class

       supply of warm water

       supply of cold water

For each group of four students

  2 plastic cups (9-ounce)

  1 plastic syringe

  1 plastic cup with circular depression

  1 small vial with 2-holed cap

  1 bottle of red food coloring

 20 paper clips

  3 textbooks

     paper towels and/or a sponge

PROCEDURE

Part A: Investigating Convection

1. Fill two 9-ounce plastic cups, one with warm water and the other with cold water.

2. Snap the small vial (cap-side up) into the base of the plastic cup that has a circular depression, as shown at right.

Capped Vial in Cup

3. Gently remove the cap, and place 1 drop of food coloring into the bottom of the vial. Carefully and firmly re-cap the vial with the 2-holed cap.

4. Use the syringe to carefully fill the vial with about 5 mL of warm water. Gently tap the vial to remove any air bubbles.

5. Cover the holes in the 2-holed cap with your fingers, and have one person in your group slowly add cold water to the setup until it is almost full.

6. Remove your fingers, and observe what happens from both the side and the top.

7. Record your observations as Trial 1 in your science notebook. Draw a labeled picture, and use arrows to sketch the movement of the colored water.

8. After a few minutes, carefully remove the vial from the cup. Describe the contents of the vial in your science notebook.

9. Empty and rinse the vial, the cap, and the cup.

10. Repeat Steps 3–9, but this time use *cold* water in Step 4 and *warm* water in Step 5. Record your observations as Trial 2. Draw a labeled picture, and use arrows to sketch the movement of the colored water.

11. Respond to Analysis items 1 and 2 in your notebook.

Part B: Investigating Gravity

12. To make a model lithospheric plate, each member of your group will link five paper clips together.

13. Link your four chains together to make one long chain of 20 paper clips. This is your model lithospheric plate.

14. Place your paper clip chain on the top of your desk in a straight line perpendicular to the edge of the desk. The end of the chain should be touching the edge of the desk.

15. Gently push one paper clip from the chain over the edge of the table. Observe what happens.

16. Repeat Step 15 until the entire chain is pulled over the edge. In your notebook, describe what you observed.

    • How many paper clips did you push over the edge before the entire chain was pulled to the floor?

    • What caused the rest of the paper clip chain to be pulled over the edge?

17. Separate all of the paper clips, except for a chain of three paper clips.

18. Make a ramp using your three textbooks by stacking two on the table, and leaning the third against the stack.

19. Place the paper clip chain at the top of the ramp so that the chain points down the ramp.

20. Release the paper clip chain. Record your observations in your notebook. What caused the paper clip chain to be pulled down the ramp?

21. Separate all of the paper clips, and return them to your supply bin.

22. Respond to Analysis items 3–6 in your notebook.

ANALYSIS

1. Use your observations from Part A to answer the following questions:

    a. Did both trials result in the movement of water? Why or why not?

    b. What do you think is necessary for convection to happen?

2. Imagine that hotter material is lying beneath an area of cooler material deep in Earth's mantle. What do you predict will happen? Be as specific as you can, and explain your reasoning.

3. What do scientists believe causes plates to move? Explain your ideas using your observations from Part A and Part B.

4. What evidence do we have that the lithospheric plates that make up Earth's surface have moved? Include at least three different types of evidence, and for each,

    • describe what the evidence is.

    • describe where the evidence was found.

    • explain how the evidence supports the idea that the plates have moved.

    Hint: Revisit your learning from the last three activities. What evidence have you learned about that supports the theory of plate tectonics?

5. Lithospheric plates move at a rate of around 5 cm per year. If we were able to place a barrel of nuclear waste in a trench, how far will it have moved in kilometers in 250,000 years (by the time the nuclear waste is no longer hazardous)?

    Hint: There are 100 cm in 1 m, and 1,000 m in 1 km.

6. **Reflection:** Geologists may never be able to observe directly what is happening inside Earth's mantle to drive plate motion. Why might they never be able to observe the mantle directly?

15 The Rock Cycle

INVESTIGATION

THE SURFACE OF Earth is ever changing. Some changes happen suddenly, such as volcanic eruptions or destructive landslides. Some happen more gradually, such as lithospheric plates moving and mountains forming. The geological processes that cause these changes also form different types of rock. Since scientists recommend that nuclear waste be stored deep underground, it is important to know about the different types of rock that might be under the surface.

Geologists identify rocks by their properties, including what they are made of, and give the rocks names, such as granite, obsidian, or marble. Geologists also group rocks based on how they formed. You already know how two types of rock form. Igneous rock forms when magma and lava cool and solidify. Sedimentary rock forms when sediments are pressed and glued together. A third type, **metamorphic rock,** is rock that has changed due to extreme heat and/or pressure. In this activity, you will learn more about how one type of rock becomes another in a process known as the **rock cycle**.

GUIDING QUESTION

How do rocks form?

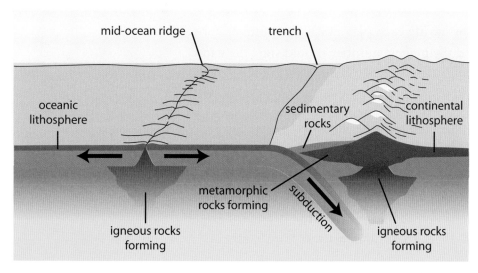

Rock forms both above and below the surface of Earth.

MATERIALS

For each group of four students

    1   Rock Cycle Game board

    1   set of 30 Igneous Rock Cards

    1   set of 30 Metamorphic Rock Cards

    1   set of 30 Sedimentary Rock Cards

    1   set of 9 Geological Process Cards

    4   game pieces

    1   number cube

For each student

    1   Student Sheet 15.1, "Geologist's Notes"

    1   Student Sheet 15.2, "Rock Formation"

PROCEDURE

1. Carefully look at Student Sheet 15.1, "Geologist's Notes." During the activity, you will use this Student Sheet to keep track of what happens to your rocks and to explain how you gathered more rocks.

2. Review the Materials list to make sure you have the materials you need.

3. Give each player nine rock cards: three Igneous Rock Cards, three Metamorphic Rock Cards, and three Sedimentary Rock Cards. Sort the remaining Rock Cards by rock type, and place them on the game board in three separate stacks.

4. Place the Geological Process Cards face down on the game board in a single stack.

5. Place each person's game piece on the Start space.

6. Begin the game by having each person roll the number cube. The person who rolled the highest number should start the game.

7. The first person should toss the number cube and move that number of spaces on the game board. When someone lands on a Geological Process space, they should pick up a Geological Process Card and follow the directions. After reading a card, replace it face down at the bottom of the stack.

8. Continue taking turns and playing the Rock Cycle Game. Remember, each person should record what happens to their rocks on Student Sheet 15.1. All new rocks should also be recorded on this sheet.

9. Stop playing when the second person crosses the Start space again.

10. Your teacher will distribute Student Sheet 15.2, "Rock Formation." Work with your group and use information from all group members' Student Sheets to complete Student Sheet 15.2.

ANALYSIS

1. Create a diagram to describe the rock cycle.

   a. Start by drawing and describing igneous, metamorphic, and sedimentary rock.

   b. Draw arrows between igneous, metamorphic, and sedimentary rock to show all the ways rock can change into other types of rock.

   c. Label the arrows with the geological process that causes each change.

   d. Include the time scale of changes by labeling at least one sudden and one gradual change.

   e. Draw a star next to a geological process driven by energy from the Sun. Draw a circle next to a geological process driven by energy from Earth's hot interior.

2. You have learned that different kinds of rock are constantly formed by geological processes, but Earth's total mass stays constant. How is that possible? Explain using what you learned in this activity.

3. Which type of rock do you think would be most stable for storing nuclear waste? Explain using evidence from this activity.

16 *Rocks as a Resource*

READING

HUMANS DEPEND ON Earth for many different natural resources. Many of the natural resources people rely on form as a result of geological processes that change Earth's surface. Some of these geological processes happen quickly, but many happen over geological time. This makes their supply limited. The geological processes that form some natural resources occur only at certain locations or for a limited amount of time. This makes their supply unevenly distributed across Earth's surface. Both the uneven distribution of natural resources as well as the long periods of time required for their formation are challenges people face when finding and using Earth's natural resources.

GUIDING QUESTION

How do geological processes affect where we find rock and mineral resources?

The Chino Copper Mine in New Mexico, USA, is one location where copper is taken out of the earth.

MATERIALS

For each student

1 Student Sheet 16.1, "Directed Reading Table: Rocks as a Resource"

1 Student Sheet 1.1, "Considering Where to Store Nuclear Waste"

PROCEDURE

1. You and your partner will read about three different resources that form through geological processes.

2. Read the article with your partner. As you read, record the information about each resource on Student Sheet 16.1, "Rocks as a Resource."

READING

Granite: An Igneous Rock

Granite is a common igneous rock on Earth. The Appalachian Mountains and the Sierra Nevada are made mostly of granite. Mount Rushmore is made of granite as well. Granite is commonly used in counter tops, floor tiles, bridges, and statues.

You know that igneous rock forms both above and below Earth's surface. When a volcano erupts, lava cools and solidifies quickly on the surface to form igneous rock, such as basalt and pumice. Igneous rock also forms when magma cools and solidifies deep

Half Dome in Yosemite National Park is made of granite.

below Earth's surface. This is how granite forms. It can take millions of years for magma to cool and solidify deep underground to form granite. This geological process happens deep below Earth's surface inside the magma chamber of a volcano.

Because granite forms very slowly, the crystals that make it up form in an inter-locking arrangement, as shown in the diagram on the right. The interlocking crystals make granite hard and stable, which means it resists being broken down into sediments. The interlocking crystals make it difficult for groundwater to flow through the rock because there are few open spaces for water to flow and collect between the interlocked crystals.

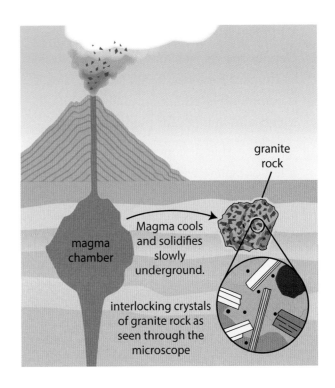

Places with granite outcrops, where large sections of granite are found on Earth's surface, typically have more granite beneath them. Because of the hardness and stability of the rock, some scientists have argued that granite outcrops make an ideal location for storing nuclear waste deep underground.

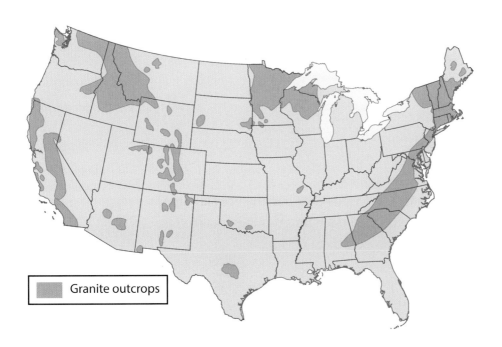

Copper: Subduction

Copper is a valuable natural resource used by humans for over 10,000 years. Today, it is commonly used in homes for electrical wiring and in pipes for plumbing.

A copper sample

You know that at convergent plate boundaries, one plate will subduct another plate. When this happens at locations where an oceanic plate goes under another plate, it drags water down along with it as it sinks into the mantle. This water is heated by thermal energy from the mantle and seeps into the cracks in the plate above. The super-heated water melts the surrounding rock. While the rock is melting, chemicals in the rock, including copper, dissolve in the water to form a solution.

As the magma and copper solution move toward the surface, away from the source of thermal energy, it cools, and the magma solidifies into crystals. The copper solution becomes more and more concentrated as the magma cools and solidifies. Eventually, the copper solution is squeezed into the cracks between the crystals in the rock. The copper solution also cools and solidifies.

Copper is formed at subduction zones.

Over geological time, these copper-containing rocks are found at the surface. They are called *metal ores* when the amount of metal in the rock is considered valuable for human use. Metal ores can also contain other valuable metals, such as gold and molybdenum. At mines, people take metal ores out of the earth and process them for use.

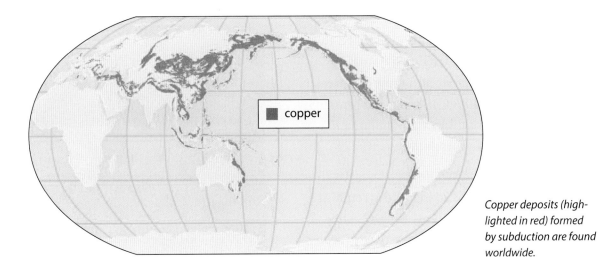

Copper deposits (high-lighted in red) formed by subduction are found worldwide.

Petroleum: A Sedimentary Process

Petroleum is a natural resource that you probably use every day. Petroleum products are used as gasoline, jet fuel, and heating oil, and as raw materials to make asphalt and plastics. It is also widely used to generate electricity.

The petroleum we use now took hundreds of millions of years to form through the geological processes that form sedimentary rock. You learned in the previous activities that sedimentary rock forms from sediments. Over time, layers of sediment pile up and are buried deep underground, where they are pressed and glued together to form sedimentary rock.

In ocean basins where there is a lot of sediment being deposited, the remains of many microorganisms are deposited with the sediments. The microorganisms, like plankton, were living in the ocean

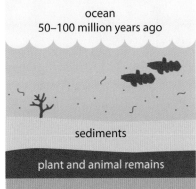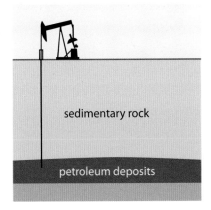

Fossil fuels, such as petroleum, formed from the remains of ancient organisms over millions of years.

and fall to the bottom when they die. Over time, the organisms' remains are buried to a significant depth under Earth's surface where pressure is higher and temperatures are warmer (66°–177°C). When the remains are under these conditions for millions to tens of millions of years, they eventually form petroleum.

Because petroleum is made of the remains of organisms, it is called a *fossil fuel*. After petroleum is taken out of the earth, it is sent to refineries where it is prepared for different uses.

Samples of petroleum on display at a museum.

Oil and Natural Gas Production in the Contiguous United States

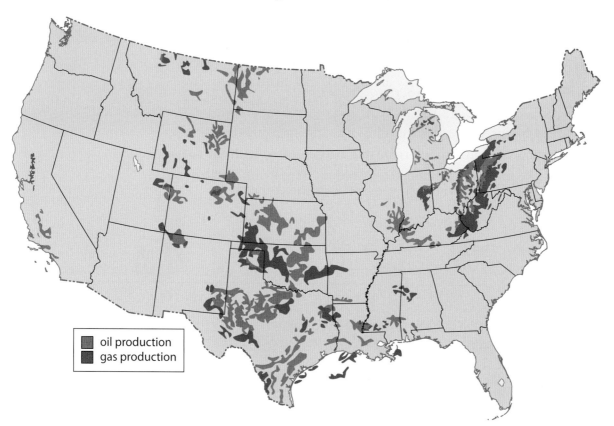

oil production
gas production

A map of locations where oil and natural gas production happens in the United States.
(USGS. Derived from Mast, et al. 1998)

ANALYSIS

1. **Nonrenewable resources** are those that cannot be replaced faster than they are used up by human populations. Do you think the resources you read about in this activity are nonrenewable? Explain why.

2. Why aren't granite, copper, or petroleum found everywhere on Earth's surface?

3. One consideration in deciding where to store nuclear waste is the presence of valuable natural resources in a proposed location. Add the consideration "Location of Natural Resources" in a new row on Student Sheet 1.1, "Considering Where to Store Nuclear Waste." In the second column, write your recommended action to take in regard to this consideration. Explain why you recommend taking this action when deciding where to store nuclear waste.

4. Your friend tells you that we don't need to consider the location of valuable natural resources when choosing a site to store nuclear waste. After all, Earth is always changing, and the processes that create these resources are still occurring. Explain how you would respond to your friend using an example from the reading.

   In your explanation, be sure to

   • indicate whether you are writing about copper, granite, or petroleum. Describe what the natural resource is used for.

   • explain the geological processes that form your natural resource and the rate at which these changes occur.

   • describe where the natural resource is found and what that says about the geological processes that happened in that area.

EXTENSION

What kinds of natural resources, formed through geological processes, exist around your home? Conduct research to find out which resources are being taken out of the earth around you, and what geological processes created those natural resources.

17 *Enough Resources for All?*

INVESTIGATION

HUMANS USE MANY natural resources. In the last activity, you learned about resources that are nonrenewable. They are limited because they form over geological time. Some examples include petroleum, metal ores such as copper, and granite. The geological processes that formed nonrenewable resources are still occurring. But it will take too long for new resources to form for them to be of use to humans in our lifetimes.

Some natural resources are **renewable**. They can be replaced as quickly as they are used by human populations. You learned about one such resource in the "Investigating Groundwater" activity. Groundwater stored in aquifers is essential to humans. Roughly 23% of freshwater used across the United States comes from groundwater. The rest comes from surface water sources. Groundwater is critical in places that lack enough surface water to meet the local population's needs. In 2010, Americans withdrew 76 billion gallons of groundwater per day. This groundwater was used for a variety of purposes, such as household water for drinking and cooking, irrigation for crops, and manufacturing.

But, even the supplies of renewable resources are not limitless. In this activity, you will explore how groundwater is used and replenished. And you will think about how the rapid growth in human population may affect access to groundwater in the future.

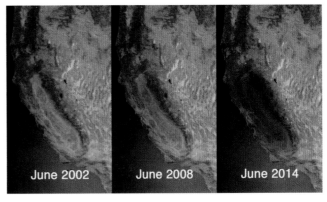

Groundwater levels in California have decreased over this time period, as indicated by the orange and red areas.

GUIDING QUESTION

How can monitoring natural resources help guide decisions about their use?

MATERIALS

For each group of four students

  1 plastic cup

28 blue game tokens

  2 red game tokens

  1 set of Aquifer Inputs and Outputs Cards

  1 Student Sheet 17.1, "Aquifer Inputs and Outputs"

  1 Student Sheet 17.2, "Graph of Groundwater Level in Our Aquifer"

For each student

  1 piece of graph paper

  1 clear metric ruler

PROCEDURE

Part A: Aquifer Inputs and Outputs

1. Place 20 blue tokens in your cup. In this model, the cup represents your community aquifer, and the tokens represent the groundwater in your aquifer. Leave the extra tokens on your table.

2. Shuffle the Aquifer Inputs and Outputs Cards, and place them face down on your table.

3. With your group of four students, use the model to learn about aquifer inputs and outputs.

   a. Decide which group member will complete each part of the model.

      • Person #1: Take one Aquifer Inputs and Outputs Card from the pile, and read all of the text on the card to your group. Each card has information about something that happened that month in your aquifer.

      • Person #2: Remove or add tokens to the aquifer cup based on the directions on the Aquifer Inputs and Outputs Card.

      • Person #3: Record what happened in the aquifer as described on the card on Student Sheet 17.1, "Aquifer Inputs and Outputs." If you removed water tokens from your aquifer, record it in the Outputs column. If you added water tokens to your aquifer, record it in the Inputs column.

      • Person #4: Count the number of tokens in your aquifer after adding or removing tokens. Plot the token or "water" level on Student Sheet 17.2, "Graph of Groundwater Level in Our Aquifer."

b. If you get a card that asks you to remove more chips than you have, remove all of your chips. Plot this point on your graph as zero. Your aquifer was empty, and your community was forced to buy water from another source.

c. Your aquifer can hold only 28 tokens. If you get a card asking you to add more tokens than will fit in your aquifer model, add tokens until you have 28, and do not use the remaining tokens. Your aquifer was full, and the rest of the water stayed on the surface and didn't add to your aquifer.

4. Repeat Step 3 above until you have drawn seven cards.

5. To have enough water for everyone in your community, you will need to have at least 15 water tokens in your aquifer. Draw a horizontal line at 15 tokens on Student Sheet 17.1.

6. With your group, observe and discuss the patterns you see in your graph on Student Sheet 17.2. What patterns do you notice in the graph? How did the amount of water in the aquifer change over time? Use evidence from the graph to support your ideas.

7. Leave your graph and your aquifer model on your table. Follow your teacher's directions to observe aquifers from other groups.

8. Respond to Analysis items 1–3 in your science notebook.

Part B: Monitoring Aquifer Levels

9. On the next page are four sets of data on the depth (below Earth's surface) to aquifer water levels from four counties in the state of California over time. The map to the right shows the locations of the four counties in the state of California. Decide with your group members which group member will graph each data set.

10. Create a line graph for your data.

Depth to Groundwater Level by Year in Santa Barbara County, CA

LOCATION: SANTA BARBARA COUNTY, CA	YEAR									
	2008	2009	2010	2011	2012	2013	2014	2015	2016	2017
Depth To Groundwater Level (Meters Below Land Surface)	94	95	95	95	94	95	96	98	99	100

Depth to Groundwater Level by Year in Imperial County, CA

LOCATION: IMPERIAL COUNTY, CA	YEAR									
	2008	2009	2010	2011	2012	2013	2014	2015	2016	2017
Depth To Groundwater Level (Meters Below Land Surface)	45	44	44	43	42	42	41	40	39	37

Depth to Groundwater Level by Year in Siskiyou County, CA

LOCATION: SISKIYOU COUNTY, CA	YEAR									
	2008	2009	2010	2011	2012	2013	2014	2015	2016	2017
Depth To Groundwater Level (Meters Below Land Surface)	48	49	52	49	50	50	51	52	52	51

Depth to Groundwater Level by Year in Inyo County, CA

LOCATION: INYO COUNTY, CA	YEAR									
	2008	2009	2010	2011	2012	2013	2014	2015	2016	2017
Depth To Groundwater Level (Meters Below Land Surface)	9	9	10	10	10	10	10	10	10	10

11. What happened to the water level in the aquifer you graphed in Step 10 over time? Use information from Student Sheet 17.2 and Analysis item 1 to provide a possible explanation for the trends in your graph. Record your ideas and data to support your claim in your notebook.

    Hint: Your graph represents how far below the surface of Earth you have to go before you hit the water level in the aquifer. This means that the larger the number and the higher the point you plot, the deeper you have to dig into Earth before you reach the water level in the aquifer.

12. Take turns sharing with your group your completed graph and the possible explanation for the trends in your graph. As your group members share, listen to each explanation to make sure it fits their graph.

ANALYSIS

1. What activities from Part A increased the groundwater level in your model aquifer? What activities caused aquifer levels to decrease? Make a list of each in your notebook.

2. Which of the inputs and outputs from Part A will increase as human population continues to grow? How do you think a larger human population will impact aquifer groundwater levels?

3. In science, we use models to help us understand cause-and-effect relationships in systems, but all models have strengths and weaknesses.

   a. What are strengths of this model? Explain your reasoning.

   b. What are weaknesses of this model? Explain your reasoning.

4. A friend tells you that we don't need to consider the location of aquifers when choosing a site to store nuclear waste. Your friend explains that this is because the groundwater stored in aquifers is a renewable resource. That means the supply of it will be replenished as quickly as people use it. Explain how you would respond to your friend.

   In your explanation, be sure to

   - explain what an aquifer is and the geological processes that form aquifers.

   - describe where aquifers form and what that says about the geological processes that happened in that area.

   - describe the activities that cause groundwater levels to increase and decrease, as well as the rate at which these changes occur.

   - explain how nuclear waste stored underground can affect groundwater in aquifers.

EXTENSION

Around the world, approximately 780 million people lack access to clean drinking water, and another 2.5 billion lack access to sanitation facilities. Conduct research to discover where lack of access to drinking water and sanitation have the biggest impacts. What are the impacts? What is already being done, and what more can be done? Visit the *SEPUP Third Edition Geological Processes* page of the SEPUP website at *www.sepuplhs.org/middle/third-edition* for links to help you begin your research.

18 *Evaluating Site Risk*

TALKING IT OVER

IN THE FIRST activity of this unit, you learned about the nuclear waste storage problem in the United States. Throughout this unit, you have learned about what must be considered when deciding where to store nuclear waste. Based on current recommendations by experts, it is likely that the country will search for one or two sites to build underground facilities for the long-term storage of nuclear waste. In this activity, you will gather data about four sites being considered for the long-term storage of nuclear waste.

The United States wants to have a long-term storage facility for nuclear waste selected and built by 2040. Use what you have learned in this unit to help you evaluate four possible sites under consideration. Which site would you recommend for further study? What are the trade-offs of your recommendation?

GUIDING QUESTION

How can we use evidence to decide where to store nuclear waste?

MATERIALS

For each group of four students

    1   Student Sheet 18.1, "Four Proposed Sites"

For each student

    1   Student Sheet 1.1, "Considering Where to Store Nuclear Waste" (completed)

    1   Student Sheet 18.1, "Four Proposed Sites"

    1   Student Sheet 18.2, "Comparing Four Proposed Sites"

    1   Student Sheet 18.3, "Discussion Web: Evaluating Site Risk"

PROCEDURE

1. Work with your group of four to complete this activity. Remember to listen to and consider the ideas of the other members of your group. If you disagree with others in your group, explain why you disagree.

2. Your teacher will distribute Student Sheet 18.1, "Four Proposed Sites." This map shows the locations of the four proposed sites for long-term storage of nuclear waste.

3. In this activity, you will gather and analyze data about each site from eight maps on the following pages. First, look at each map and its key carefully. Then, look for patterns across the maps. Discuss how any patterns you see might influence your choice of a site to store nuclear waste.

4. Split your group of four into pairs. Assign each pair two of the four sites from Student Sheet 18.1 to learn more about.

5. Work with your partner to gather data about your two sites from each of the eight maps on the pages that follow. Record the data in the table on Student Sheet 18.2, "Comparing Four Proposed Sites."

6. After you and your partner gather data about your two sites, return to your group of four to share what you learned. Listen as the other pair shares what they learned. As you listen, record data about the other two sites to complete the table on Student Sheet 18.2.

7. With your group, discuss the similarities and differences in the data between the four sites using Student Sheet 18.2. Discuss the advantages and disadvantages of each site.

8. Work with your group to come to an agreement about which of the four sites should be studied further.

9. Complete Student Sheet 18.3, "Discussion Web: Evaluating Site Risk." Use your data from the maps as evidence to support your decision about why this site should be studied further. Discuss the trade-offs of your decision.

10. Present your group's recommendation to the class.

Map 1: Population Density by County in the Contiguous U.S.

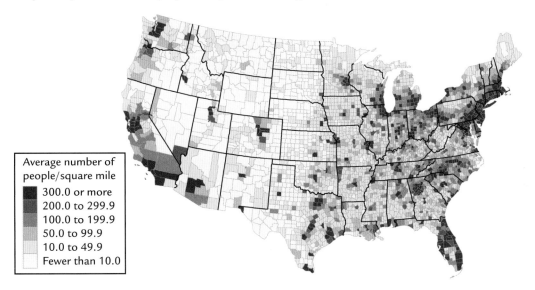

Average number of people/square mile
300.0 or more
200.0 to 299.9
100.0 to 199.9
50.0 to 99.9
10.0 to 49.9
Fewer than 10.0

Map 2: Locations of Operating Nuclear Reactors in the Contiguous U.S.

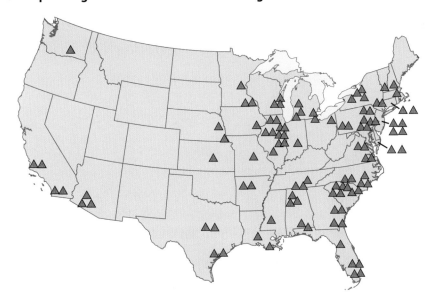

Map 3: Landslide Hazards in the Contiguous U.S.

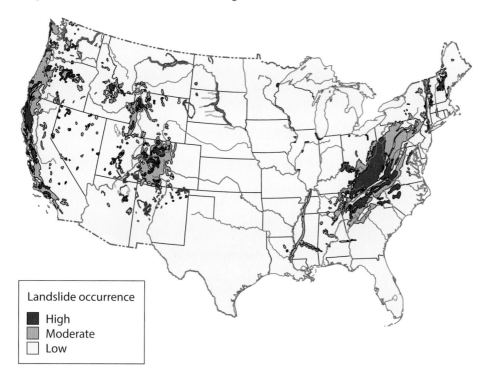

Landslide occurrence
High
Moderate
Low

Map 4: Earthquake Hazards in the Contiguous U.S.

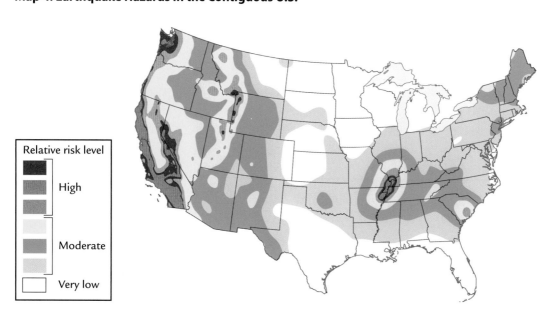

Relative risk level
High
Moderate
Very low

Map 5: Volcano Hazards in the Contiguous U.S.

Map 6: Granite Outcrops in the Contiguous U.S

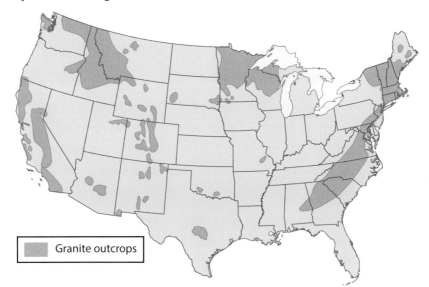

Map 7: Aquifers in the Contiguous U.S.

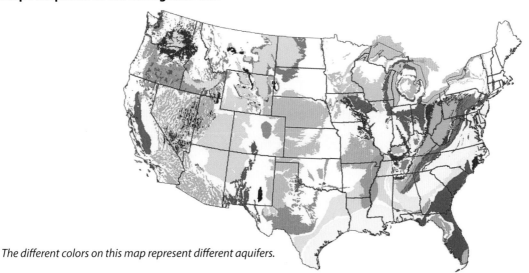

The different colors on this map represent different aquifers.

Map 8: Metal Ore mines in the Contiguous U.S.

ANALYSIS

1. Choose a natural hazard that you learned about in this unit. If you had to build a long-term storage facility for nuclear waste in an area of high risk of this natural hazard, how could you use technology to protect the facility from these types of geological events? Explain your ideas.

2. What role do you think people in the community should have when a site near them has been suggested for storing nuclear waste?

3. Which of the four sites would you recommend for further study?

    a. State the site you would choose.

    b. Support your decision with as many pieces of evidence as you can.

    c. Discuss the trade-offs of your decision.

4. **Reflection**: Have your ideas changed during this unit about where to store nuclear waste? How?

EXTENSION

Is there a different site that you would suggest for further study?
Look at each of the maps again, and determine if there is a site that is
better than the four you learned about in this activity. Write why you
would select this site over the four you learned about in the lesson.
Support your decision with as many pieces of evidence as you can,
and discuss the trade-offs of your decision.

Geological Processes

UNIT SUMMARY

Changes to Earth's Surface

Geological processes cause changes to Earth's surface. Changes can happen suddenly or gradually. Earth's surface can change suddenly during events such as landslides. Landslides occur when rock, soil, and other earth materials flow rapidly down a slope. Other changes take millions of years, such as geological processes that form mountain ranges or that form different types of rock. Geological processes can affect smaller, local areas or can cause global changes.

Natural Hazards

Many geological processes cause natural hazards. Intense rainfall, ground-shaking from earthquakes, or volcanic eruptions can cause landslides. Landslides can destroy homes and villages and close roads and bridges. Some volcanic eruptions eject huge amounts of ash into the atmosphere. Wind can carry the ash long distances. When the ash falls, it can make travel difficult and cause health problems for people. Another natural hazard is ground-shaking during an earthquake. Intense ground-shaking can cause buildings and other structures to fail.

Scientists use equipment to monitor areas where natural hazards happen often. These data allow scientists to better understand why these events happen. The information also helps to improve scientists' predictions about when events will occur. Technology has allowed us to design buildings that can withstand ground-shaking and develop early warning systems to minimize the impact of natural hazards.

Plate Tectonics

Volcanic activity and earthquakes happen in global patterns. This is because Earth's surface is broken into lithospheric plates, which are solid pieces of the upper mantle and crust, that move. By mapping the movement of Earth's plates using GPS technology, scientists know that plates move at an average rate of 5–10 cm per year. At plate boundaries, places where two or more plates meet, the moving plates interact. At transform plate boundaries, plates move past each other, which causes earthquakes. At convergent plate boundaries, plates move past each other. The interactions at convergent plate boundaries can causes earthquakes, volcanoes, and the formation of large mountain ranges. Plates moving away from each other at divergent boundaries form volcanoes and cause earthquakes.

Earth's lithospheric plates have moved over geological time, drastically changing the appearance of Earth's surface. Alfred Wegener was one of the first scientists to collect data suggesting that Earth's continents hadn't always been where they are today. He published the idea he called *continental drift* in 1912. Wegner cited evidence to support his ideas, includings the existence of the same fossils on distant continents, similar rock types and layers on distant continents, and how the continents seemed to fit together like puzzle pieces. Wegener used this evidence to argue that the continents once formed one large supercontinent, which he named Pangea. He could not explain how the continents had moved, so the scientific community rejected his idea of moving continents over geological time.

Later, scientists developed the ability to map the ocean floor. They discovered long underwater chains of volcanoes called *mid-ocean ridges*. Scientists also found deep trenches on the ocean floor near convergent plate boundaries. Wegener's fossil and rock-type evidence, along with the new evidence about mid-ocean ridges and trenches, led to the theory of plate tectonics. Plate tectonics is the theory that Earth's lithospheric plates are in constant motion. Evidence suggests that the two forces driving it are convection in the mantle and gravity.

Rocks and the Rock Cycle

Rocks can become other types of rock through geological processes, some of which are related to plate motion. Igneous rock forms when magma cools and solidifies, either during a volcanic eruption or deep underground. Metamorphic rock forms deep underground as the extreme pressure and/or temperatures change existing rock. One area where metamorphic rock forms is at convergent plate boundaries. Sedimentary rocks form when sediments are pressed and glued together. All types of rock can be transformed into all other types of rock in a process called the *rock cycle*.

Distribution of Earth's Natural Resources

Many natural resources that humans rely on form through geological processes that take place over geological time. For example, granite is a natural resource used in counter tops and statues. It is an igneous rock, formed underground as magma slowly cools, sometimes over millions of years. Because these kinds of natural resources take millions of years to form, they are considered nonrenewable. Additionally, the same geological processes do not happen across all of Earth's surface. Thus, natural resources are not found everywhere.

Other natural resources are considered renewable. Groundwater collects in aquifers. It is renewable because it is quickly replenished when it rains, when snow or ice melts, or through river and stream water seepage. Like other natural resources, the geological processes that form and replenish groundwater supplies do not happen evenly across Earth's surface.

Essential Scientific Terms

earthquake

geological time

lithospheric plate

mid-ocean ridge

natural hazards

natural resource

plate boundary

plate tectonics

rock cycle

trench

volcano

THE NATURE OF SCIENCE AND ENGINEERING

IF **SOMEONE ASKED YOU** the question, "What is science?" how would you answer?

You might reply that it is knowledge of such subjects as Biology, Chemistry, Earth Science, and Physics. That would be only partly correct. Although science is certainly related to the accumulation and advancement of knowledge, it is much more than that. Science is a way of exploring and understanding the natural world.

According to the American Association for the Advancement of Science (AAAS), two of the most fundamental aspects of science are that the world is understandable and that scientific ideas are subject to change.

Scientists believe that the world is understandable because things happen in consistent patterns that we can eventually understand through careful study. Observations must be made and data collected for us to discover the patterns that exist in the universe. At times scientists have to invent the instruments that allow them to collect this data. Eventually, they develop theories to explain the observations and patterns. The principles on which a theory is based apply throughout the universe.

When new knowledge becomes available, it is sometimes necessary to change theories. This most often means making small adjustments, but on rare occasions it means completely revising a theory. Although scientists can never be 100% certain about a theory, as knowledge about the universe becomes more sophisticated most theories become more refined and more widely accepted. You will see examples of this process as you study the history of scientists' understanding of such topics as elements and the periodic table, the cellular basis of life, genetics, plate tectonics, the solar system, and the universe in this middle school science program.

While the main goal of science is to understand phenomena, the main goal of engineering is to solve problems. Like science, engineering involves both knowledge and a set of practices common across a range of engineering problems. Just as scientists start by asking questions, engineers start by defining problems. Just as scientists search for explanations for phenomena, engineers search for solutions to problems.

Science and engineering often build on each other. For example, scientists use instruments developed by engineers to study the natural world. And engineers use scientific principles when designing solutions to problems.

Scientific Inquiry

Inquiry is at the heart of science, and an important component of inquiry is scientific investigation, including experimentation. Although scientists do not necessarily follow a series of fixed steps when conducting investigations, they share common understandings about the characteristics of a scientifically valid investigation. For example, scientists obtain evidence from observations and measurements. They repeat and confirm observations and ask other scientists to review their results. It is important for scientists to avoid bias in designing, conducting, and reporting their investigations and to have other unbiased scientists duplicate their results. Some types of investigations allow scientists to set up controls and vary just one condition at a time. They formulate and test hypotheses, sometimes collecting data that lead them to develop theories.

When scientists develop theories they are constructing models and explanations of the patterns and relationships they observe in natural phenomena. These explanations must be logically consistent with the evidence they have gathered and with evidence other scientists have gathered. Hypotheses and theories allow scientists to make predictions. If testing turns out to not support a prediction, scientists may have to look at revising the hypothesis or theory on which the prediction was based.

Engineering Design

An engineer uses science and technology to build a product or design a process that solves a problem or makes the world better. Engineering design refers to the process engineers use to design, test, and improve solutions to problems. Like scientists, engineers design investigations to test their ideas, use mathematics, analyze their data, and develop models.

Since most solutions in the real world are not perfect, engineers work to develop the best solutions they can, while balancing such factors as the function, cost, safety, and usability of their solutions. The factors engineers identify as important for solutions to a problem are called criteria and constraints. Most engineering solutions have one or more trade-offs—desired features that must be given up in order to gain other more desirable features.

Science as a Human Endeavor

Science and engineering are human activities. People from all over the world engage in science and engineering and use scientific information and technological solutions. The types of questions a scientist asks and the types of problems an engineer tries to solve are influenced by what they think is important. And what they think is important to investigate often depends on their background, experiences, and perspective. This is why it is essential for all types of people to become scientists and engineers—to be sure science and engineering respond to their interests and needs and to be sure that there are diverse ideas to enrich explanations and arguments. Participation by a wide variety of people in science and engineering will lead to greater and swifter progress toward understanding how the natural world works and solving problems facing individuals, communities, and the environment.

Visit the *SEPUP Third Edition* page for each unit of the SEPUP website at *www.sepuplhs.org/middle/third-edition* to learn more about the interests and accomplishments of diverse scientists and engineers. Each unit highlights examples of people from varied backgrounds in careers that contribute to and depend on the advancement of science and technology.

References

American Association for the Advancement of Science (AAAS). (1990). Project 2061: Science for all Americans. New York: Oxford University Press.

National Research Council. (2012). *A Framework for K–12 Science Education: Practices, Crosscutting Concepts, and Core Ideas*. Committee on a Conceptual Framework for New K–12 Science Education Standards. Board on Science Education, Division of Behavioral and Social Sciences and Education. Washington, DC: The National Academies Press.

B Science Safety

SCIENCE SAFETY GUIDELINES

YOU ARE RESPONSIBLE for your own safety and for the safety of others. Be sure you understand the following guidelines and follow your teacher's instructions for all laboratory and field activities.

Before the Investigation

- Listen carefully to your teacher's instructions, and follow any steps recommended when preparing for the activity.

- Know the location and proper use of emergency safety equipment, such as the safety eye-and-face wash, fire blanket, and fire extinguisher.

- Know the location of exits and the procedures for an emergency.

- Dress appropriately for lab work. Tie back long hair and avoid wearing dangling or bulky jewelry or clothing. Do not wear open-toed shoes. Avoid wearing synthetic fingernails—they are a fire hazard and can tear protective gloves.

- Tell your teacher if you wear contact lenses, have allergies to latex, food, or other items, or have any medical condition that may affect your ability to perform the lab safely.

- Make sure the worksurface and floor in your work area are clear of books, backpacks, purses, or other unnecessary materials.

- Ask questions if you do not understand the procedure or safety recommendations for an activity.

- Review, understand, and sign the Safety Agreement, and obtain the signature of a parent or guardian.

During the Investigation

- Carefully read and follow the activity procedure and safety recommendations.

- Follow any additional written and spoken instructions provided by your teacher.

- Use only those activities and materials approved by your teacher and needed for the investigation.

- Don't eat, drink, chew gum, or apply cosmetics in the lab area.

- Wear personal protective equipment (chemical splash goggles, lab aprons, and protective gloves) appropriate for the activity.

- Do not wear contact lenses when using chemicals. If your doctor says you must wear them, notify your teacher before conducting any activity that uses chemicals.

- Read all labels on chemicals, and be sure you are using the correct chemical.

- Keep chemical containers closed when not in use.

- Do not touch, taste, or smell any chemical unless you are instructed to do so by your teacher.

- Mix chemicals only as directed.

- Use caution when working with hot plates, hot liquids, electrical equipment, and glassware.

- Follow all directions when working with live organisms or microbial cultures.

- Be mature and cautious, and don't engage in horseplay.

- Report any unsafe situations, accidents, or chemical spills to your teacher immediately.

- If you spill chemicals on your skin, wash it for 15 minutes with large amounts of water. Remove any contaminated clothing and continue to rinse. Ask your teacher if you should take other steps, including seeking medical attention.

- Respect and take care of all equipment.

After the Investigation

- Dispose of all chemical and biological materials as instructed by your teacher.

- Clean up your work area, replace bottle caps securely, and follow any special instructions.

- Return equipment to its proper location.

- Wash your hands with soap and warm water for at least 20 seconds after any laboratory activity, even if you wore protective gloves.

Your teacher will give you an agreement similar to the one below to sign.

Science Safety Agreement

STUDENT

I, _____, have read the attached Science Safety Guidelines for students and have discussed them in my classroom. I understand my responsibilities for maintaining safety in the science classroom. I agree to follow these guidelines and any additional rules provided by the school district or my teacher.

Student Signature_____

Date_____

PARENT OR GUARDIAN

Please review with your student the attached Science Safety Guidelines, which include the safety responsibilities and expectations for all students. It is important that all students follow these guidelines in order to protect themselves, their classmates, and their teachers from accidents. Please contact the school if you have any questions about these guidelines.

I, _____, have read the attached guidelines and discussed them with my child. I understand that my student is responsible for following these guidelines and any additional instructions at all times.

Parent or Guardian Signature_____

Date_____

C Science Skills

THE FOLLOWING PAGES include instructional sheets that you can use to review important science skills:

- Reading a Graduated Cylinder
- Using a Dropper Bottle
- Bar Graphing Checklist
- Scatterplot and Line Graphing Checklist
- Interpreting Graphs
- Elements of Good Experimental Design
- Using Microscopes

READING A GRADUATED CYLINDER

A graduated cylinder measures the volume of a liquid, usually in milliliters (mL). To measure correctly with a graduated cylinder:

1. Determine what measurement each unmarked line on the graduated cylinder represents.

2. Set the graduated cylinder on a flat surface and pour in the liquid to be measured.

3. Bring your eyes to the level of the fluid's surface. (You will need to bend down!)

4. Read the graduated cylinder at the lowest point of the liquid's curve (called the *meniscus*).

5. If the curve falls between marks, estimate the volume to the closest milliliter.

The example below shows a plastic graduated cylinder that contains 42 mL of liquid.

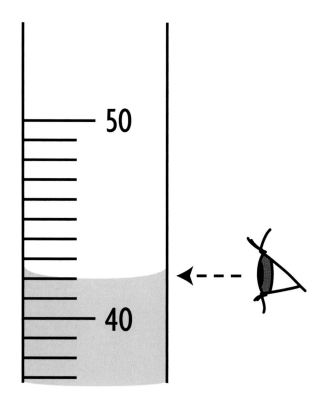

USING A DROPPER BOTTLE

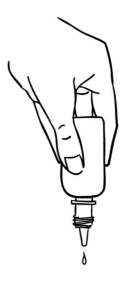

Incorrect

Holding the dropper bottle at an angle creates drops that vary in size.

Correct

Holding the dropper bottle vertically creates drops that are more consistent in size.

BAR GRAPHING CHECKLIST

Sample Graph

Follow the instructions below to make a sample bar graph.

☐ Start with a table of data. This table represents the amount of Chemical A that the Acme Company used each year from 2011 to 2015.

Year	Chemical A used (kg)
2011	100
2012	80
2013	110
2014	90
2015	105

☐ Determine whether a bar graph is the best way to represent the data.

☐ If so, draw the axes. Label them with the names and units of the data.

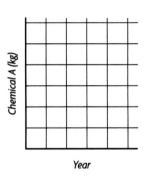

☐ Decide on a scale for each axis. Be sure there is enough space for all the data and that it's not too crowded.

Year axis: *1 block = 1 year*
Chemical A axis: *1 block = 20 kilograms*

☐ Mark intervals on the graph, and label them clearly.

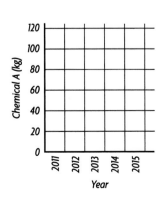

BAR GRAPHING CHECKLIST (continued)

☐ Plot your data on the graph.

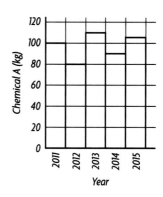

☐ Fill in the bars.

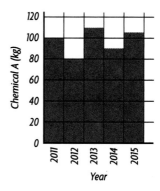

☐ Title your graph. The title should describe what the graph shows.

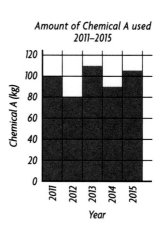

SCATTERPLOT AND LINE GRAPHING CHECKLIST

Sample Graph

Follow the instructions below to make a sample graph.

MOTION OF A BALL

Time (minutes)	Distance (meters)
0	0
1	5
2	9
3	16
4	20
5	27

☐ Start with a table of data.

☐ Determine whether a line graph or a scatterplot is the best way to represent the data.

LINE GRAPH

☐ Draw the axes. Label them with the names and units of the data.

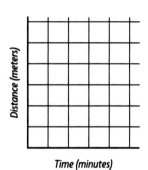

Time (minutes)

☐ Decide on a scale for each axis. Be sure there is enough space for all the data and that it's not too crowded.

Time axis: 1 block = 1 minute

Distance axis: 1 block = 5 meters

☐ Draw intervals on the graph, and label them clearly.

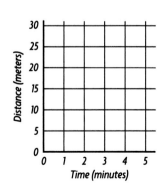

SCATTERPLOT AND LINE GRAPHING CHECKLIST (continued)

☐ Plot your data on the graph.

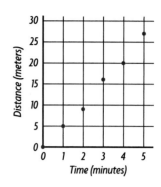

☐ For a scatterplot, leave the points unconnected.

For a line graph, draw a smooth line or curve that follows the pattern indicated by the position of the points.

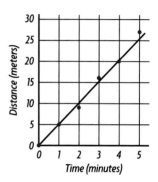

☐ Title your graph. The title should describe what the graph shows.

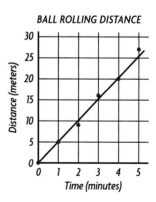

☐ If more than one data set has been plotted, include a key.

● = large ball
○ = small ball

INTERPRETING GRAPHS

Determine the path that describes the data.

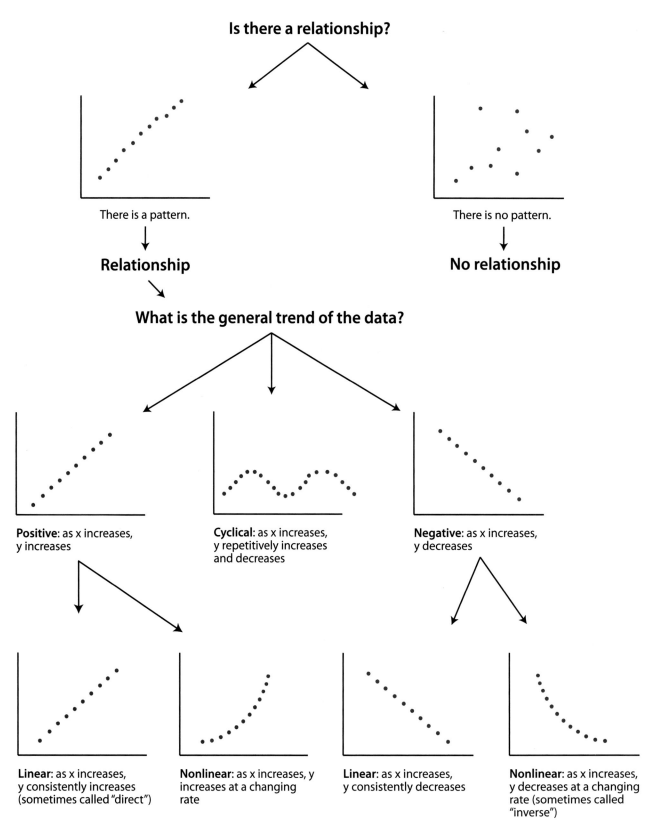

Is there a relationship?

There is a pattern.

There is no pattern.

Relationship

No relationship

What is the general trend of the data?

Positive: as x increases, y increases

Cyclical: as x increases, y repetitively increases and decreases

Negative: as x increases, y decreases

Linear: as x increases, y consistently increases (sometimes called "direct")

Nonlinear: as x increases, y increases at a changing rate

Linear: as x increases, y consistently decreases

Nonlinear: as x increases, y decreases at a changing rate (sometimes called "inverse")

INTERPRETING GRAPHS (continued)

Define the components of the graph.

Things you can say:

"The title of the graph is ..."

"The independent variable in this graph is ..."

"The dependent variable in this graph is ..."

"_____ is measured in _____"

Create a description of what the graph reveals.

Things you can say:

"This graph shows that ..."

"As the _____ increases, the ..."

"The _____ has the highest ..."

"_____ is different from _____ because ..."

"The_____ peaked at ..."

"The rate of _____ increased from ..."

Describe how the graph relates to the topic.

Things you can say:

"This graph is important to understanding _____because ..."

"This graph supports the claim that _____ because ..."

"This graph refutes the claim that _____ because ..."

ELEMENTS OF GOOD EXPERIMENTAL DESIGN

An experiment that is well designed

- builds on previous research.

- is based on a question, observation, or hypothesis.

- describes all steps in a procedure clearly and completely.

- includes a control for comparison.

- keeps all variables—except the one being tested—the same.

- describes all data to be collected.

- includes precise measurements and all records of data collected during experiment.

- may require multiple trials.

- can be reproduced by other investigators.

- respects human and animal subjects.

Note: Elements may vary depending on the problem being studied.

USING MICROSCOPES

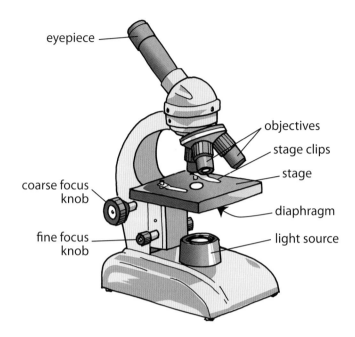

eyepiece

objectives

stage clips

stage

coarse focus knob

diaphragm

fine focus knob

light source

Focusing a Microscope

Be sure that your microscope is set on the lowest power before placing your slide onto the microscope stage. Place the slide on the microscope stage. Center the slide so that the sample is directly over the light opening, and adjust the microscope settings as necessary. If the microscope has stage clips, secure the slide in position so that it does not move.

- Observe the sample. Focus first with the coarse-focus knob, and then adjust the fine-focus knob.

- After switching to a higher power magnification, be careful to adjust the focus with the fine-focus knob only.

- Return to low power before removing the slide from the microscope stage.

Safety

Always carry a microscope properly with both hands—one hand underneath and one holding the microscope arm. When you are working with live organisms, be sure to wash your hands thoroughly after you finish the laboratory.

Some Tips for Better Drawings

- Use a sharp pencil and have a good eraser available.

- Try to relax your eyes when looking through the eyepiece. You can cover one eye or learn to look with both eyes open. Try not to squint.

- Look through your microscope at the same time as you do your drawing. Look through the microscope more than you look at your paper.

- Don't draw every small thing on your slide. Just concentrate on one or two of the most common or interesting things.

- You can draw things larger than you actually see them. This helps you show all of the details you see.

- Keep written words outside the circle.

- Use a ruler to draw the lines for your labels. Keep lines parallel— do not cross one line over another.

- Remember to record the level of magnification next to your drawing.

Spirogyra (algae) x 400

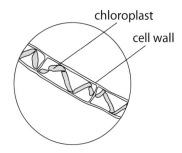

chloroplast

cell wall

The International System of Units

MEASUREMENTS THAT APPEAR in this program are expressed in metric units from the International System of Units, otherwise known as *SI units* (from Système Internationale d'Unités), which was established by international agreement. Virtually all countries in the world mandate use of the metric system exclusively. The United States does not use the metric system for many measurements, although it has been the standard for the scientific community in the United States for more than 200 years. A U.S. government effort to convert from the United States customary system to metric measurements in all realms of life has yet to extend far beyond governmental agencies, the military, and some industries.

The reason that many countries have replaced their traditional measurement systems with the metric system is its ease of use and to improve international trade. There are far fewer units to understand in comparison to the system commonly used in the United States. The metric system has only one base unit for each quantity and larger or smaller units are expressed by adding a prefix. The table below shows the base units in the International System of Units.

QUANTITY	BASE UNIT
Length	meter (m)
Mass	kilogram (kg)
Time	second (s)
Temperature	kelvin (K)
Electric current	ampere (A)
Luminous intensity	candela (cd)
Mole	mole (mol)

Other international units appearing in SEPUP's *Issues and Science* units are shown in the table below:

QUANTITY	UNIT	COMMON EXAMPLE
Temperature	Celsius (°C)	Room temperature is about 20° Celsius
Volume	liter (L)	A large soda bottle contains 2 liters.
Mass	gram (g)	A dollar bill has the mass of about 1 gram.
Wavelength	nanometer (nm)	Visible light is in the range of 400 to 780 nanometers

The International System's prefixes change the magnitude of the units by factors of 1,000. Prefixes indicate which multiple of a thousand is applied. For example, the prefix *kilo-* means 1,000. Therefore, a kilometer is 1,000 meters and a kilogram is 1,000 grams. To convert a quantity from one unit to another in the metric system, the quantity needs only to be multiplied or divided by multiples of 1,000. The chart below shows the prefixes for the metric system in relation to the base units. *Note*: Although it is not a multiple of 1,000 the prefix *centi-* is commonly used, for example, in the unit centimeter. Centi- represents a factor of one 100th.

METRIC PREFIX	FACTOR	FACTOR (NUMERICAL)
giga (G)	one billion	1,000,000,000
mega (M)	one million	1,000,000
kilo (k)	one thousand	1,000
[UNIT]	one	1
milli (m)	one one-thousandth	1/1,000
micro (μ)	one one-millionth	1/1,000,000
nano (n)	one one-billionth	1/1,000,000,000

E

Literacy Strategies

THE FOLLOWING PAGES include instructional sheets and templates for some of the literacy strategies that are used throughout this book. Use them for reference or to copy into your science notebook.

- Oral Presentations
- Reading Scientific Procedures
- Keeping a Science Notebook
- Writing a Formal Investigation Report
- Constructing a Concept Map
- Developing Communication Skills

ORAL PRESENTATIONS

- Your presentation time is short. Focus your presentation on the most important ideas you need to communicate.

- Communicate clearly by planning your words in advance. When speaking, talk slowly and loudly, and look at your audience.

- Group members should ask for and give each other support if they need help expressing a key word or concept.

- Include graphs and maps when possible. Make sure the type or handwriting and the images are large enough for everyone in the audience to see them.

- While you have your own opinions on a topic, it is important that you present unbiased and complete information. Your audience can then make their own conclusions.

- All the members of a group must participate.

- Since any group member may be asked to answer questions from the class, all group members should fully understand the presentation.

- In a group presentation, you could all play the role of different experts when presenting your information. The class would represent the community members who might be making a decision on the issue.

READING SCIENTIFIC PROCEDURES

The purpose of reading a scientific procedure is to find out exactly what to do, when to do it and with what materials, in order to complete all the steps of an investigation.

If you read a step and are not sure what to do, try these strategies:

- Re-read the previous step.

- Re-read the step that confuses you. Sometimes re-reading clarifies the information.

- Ask your partner if he or she understands what the step says to do.

- Ask your partner if there are words you don't understand.

- Ask your partner to explain what the step says to do.

- Ask your partner to read the step aloud as you listen and try to do what your partner is describing.

- Re-read the purpose (Guiding Question) of the investigation.

- Try to say the purpose of the step out loud in your own words.

- Look at the clues in the pictures of the activity.

- Peek at other groups and listen to see if they are doing the step that confuses you.

- Tell your teacher exactly what you are confused about and why it doesn't make sense.

KEEPING A SCIENCE NOTEBOOK

- Write in blue or black ink.

- Cross out mistakes or changes with a single line. Do not erase or use correction fluid.

- Write neatly.

- Record the date of each entry.

- For each new investigation, write down the following:

  Title:

  Purpose:
  Re-write the Guiding Question in your own words.
  Hint: What are you going to do? Why are you going to do it?

  Materials:
  Place a "√" here after you have collected the necessary materials.

  Procedure:
  Write down whether you understand the procedure.

  Data:
  Record observations, measurements, and other lab work.
  Include data tables, charts, diagrams, and/or graphs when needed.
  Be sure to label your work clearly.

- Sometimes, you may want to do the following:

  Make inferences or draw conclusions based on the data.
  I think my results mean . . .
  I think that this happened because . . .

  Reflect on how the activity worked in your group.
  This is what went well . . This is what did not go well . . .
  If I could do this activity again, I would . . .

  Think about what questions you still have.
  I wonder if . . .
  I'm not sure about . . .

  Keep track of new vocabulary and ideas.
  A key word I learned is . . .
  I would like to find out what happens when . . .
  One interesting thing to do would be to . . .

KEEPING A SCIENCE NOTEBOOK

The following is a guide to help you conduct investigations. However, depending on the investigation, you may not always use all of steps below or use them in the same order each time.

Title: Choose a title that describes the investigation.

Purpose: What am I looking for? Write what you are trying to find out in the form of a question.

Background: What do I know about the topic? Write a summary of background information you have on the topic that led to the purpose for the investigation.

Hypothesis: Write a statement about what you predict you will see as data in the experiment to answer the question in the "Purpose" and why you are making that prediction.

Experimental Design: How will you answer the question?

Describe the methods you will use (what you will do) to answer the question.

Use short numbered steps that are easy to follow in the lab.

Make a list of the materials you will use to answer the question.

Outline the variables:

- Independent variable (what is being changed)
- Dependent variable (what is being measured)
- Control (what will be used as baseline comparison)

Data: What did you find?

Record observations and measurements.

Use a data table where appropriate to organize the data.

Don't forget to include proper units and clear labels.

At the end of your investigation, do the following:

Make inferences or draw conclusions about the data:

I think my results mean . . .

I think this happened because . . .

Think about any errors that occurred during the investigation:

What did not go as planned?

What steps were hard to follow while doing the investigation and why?

Think about questions you still have that could lead to new investigations:

I wonder if . . .

I'm not sure about . . .

Keep track of new vocabulary and new ideas that could lead to new investigations

I would like to find out what happens when . . .

One interesting thing to do would be to . . .

Reflect on how the activity worked in your group

This is what went well . . . This is what did not go well . . .

If I could do this investigation again, I would . . .

WRITING A FORMAL INVESTIGATION REPORT

Use the information from your science notebook to write a formal report on the investigation you performed.

Title:

Choose a title that describes the investigation.

Abstract: What were you looking for in this investigation, and what did you find?

Write a paragraph that summarizes what you already knew about the topic, your purpose, your hypothesis, and your results and conclusions.

Experimental Design:

Describe the materials and investigational methods you used to answer the question.

State what variables you worked with and any controls.

Data: What did you find?

Report observations and measurements. Include an organized data table if appropriate to help someone reviewing your report to easily see the results.

Don't forget to use proper units of measurement and write clear labels for your table columns.

Data Analysis: Represent the data in a way that can be easily interpreted.

Use graphs, diagrams, or charts where appropriate to help a reviewer interpret your data.

Conclusion: What do the data mean?

Summarize the data.

Discuss your conclusion based on the accuracy of your hypothesis and the data you collected.

Discuss any errors that occurred that may have interfered with the results.

Describe any changes that need to be made the next time the investigation is performed.

Describe any new questions to be investigated based on the results of this investigation.

CONSTRUCTING A CONCEPT MAP

1. Work with your group to create a list of 15–20 words related to the topic.

2. If you are uncertain of the meaning of a word, look it up in the book or your notes or discuss it with your group.

3. Discuss with your group how all of the words on your list are related, and sort your list of words into three to five categories based on these relationships.

   Remember to listen to and consider the ideas of other members of your group. If you disagree with others in your group, explain to the rest of the group why you disagree.

4. Identify words that can be used to describe each category.

5. Work with your group to create a concept map on this topic. Follow these steps:

   a. Write the topic in the center of your paper, and circle it.

   b. Place the words describing each category around the topic. Circle each word.

   c. Draw a line between the topic and each category. On each line, explain the relationship between the topic and the category.

   d. Repeat Steps 5b and 5c as you continue to add all of the words on your list to your concept map.

   e. Add lines to connect other related words. Explain the relationship between the words on the line.

6. View the concept maps of other groups. As you look at their concept maps, observe similarities and differences between their maps and yours. Discuss your observations with your group members.

DEVELOPING COMMUNICATION SKILLS

COMMUNICATION	SENTENCE STARTERS
To better understand	One point that was not clear to me was … Are you saying that … Can you please clarify …
To share an idea	Another idea is to … What if we tried … I have an idea. We could try …
To disagree	I see your point, but what about … Another way of looking at it is … I'm still not convinced that …
To challenge	How did you reach the conclusion that … What makes you think that … How does it explain …
To look for feedback	What would help me improve … Does it make sense, what I said about …
To provide positive feedback	One strength of your idea is … Your idea is good because … I have an idea. We coud try …
To provide constructive feedback	The argument would be stronger if … Another way to do it would be … What if you said it like this …
To discuss information presented in text and graphics	I'm not sure I completely understand this, but I think it may mean … I know something about this from … A question I have about this is … If we look at the graphic, it shows …

F *Media Literacy*

IMAGINE YOURSELF READING a magazine. A feature article summarizes recent studies on the effectiveness of vitamin supplements and concludes that taking vitamin pills and liquids is a waste of money. A few pages later, an advertisement from a vitamin company claims that one of its products will protect you from all sorts of diseases. Such wide differences in claims that you will see in the popular media are common, but how can you tell which one is correct? "Media literacy" is the term that encompasses the skills we need to develop to effectively analyze and evaluate the barrage of information we encounter every day. Media literacy also includes the ability to use various media to create and communicate our own messages.

A strong background in the process of science helps you build two important skills of media literacy: being able to identify valid and adequate evidence behind a claim and evaluating if the claim is a logical conclusion based on the evidence. The skills share much in common with the process of scientific inquiry, in which you learn to seek out information, assess the information, and come to a conclusion based on your findings.

Evaluating Media Messages

A "media message" is an electronic, digital, print, audible, or artistic visual message created to transmit information. Media messages can include newspaper articles, political advertisements, speeches, artwork, or even billboards. The following are some of the kinds of questions you might ask as you learn to critically analyze and evaluate messages from various kinds of media. On the next page are three examples of media messages, all related to a common theme. Use these three examples to analyze and evaluate the messages.

BAY MEDICAL JOURNAL

The Monthly Journal of the Bay Region Medical Society

Vol. XXXIV, No. 8

Vitamin Z reduces severity of the common cold by 15%

P. M. Chakravarty, M.D., Harbord University Medical School, Clinical Studies Department
Loretta Arrienza, Ph.D., University of the Bay Region, Department of Epidemiology
Mary S. Lowe, M.D., Mid-Bay Hospital, Director of Patient Care
William Ness, M.P.H., N.P., Mid-Bay Hospital, Director of Nursing

ABSTRACT: IN A TWELVE-MONTH STUDY with 626 healthy male and female participants aged 21–36 and located in the general Bay region, the authors found that a reg.... ...ose of Vitamin Z appeared to reduce the severity of the common cold by 15%. In this controlled ....s received a placebo, and 313 participants received a 500 mg dose of Vitamin Z ....he dose did not know which ....

BEFORE   AFTER

OUR DOCTOR-APPROVED VITAMINS PUT YOU BACK ON YOUR FEET! Try HEALTH-GLOWW TODA...

Super savings:
600 for the price of 50...
Call now! **1-999-997-...**

HOME & HEALTH Magazine

September

Are VITAMINS a WASTE of your money?

SUZANNE BERYL WALKER

Donna S. was wondering if vitamins might give her the energy and good health that she felt had been slipping away ever since she had moved to Springfield with her family for a new job.

1. Who created this message?

Is this person an expert in the content of the message? What credentials does this person have that would make them an expert in this topic? Does this person have any conflicts of interest that may make him or her biased in any way? Who sponsored (or paid for) the message? Does the source of funding have any conflicts of interest?

2. **What creative techniques in the message attract a person's attention?**

   Are there any sensational or emotional words, images, or sounds that grab the viewer's attention? Do any of these words, images, or sounds try to stir up emotions and influence the viewer's ideas?

3. **Does the message cite or mention appropriate sources of factual information?**

   Does the author cite first-person sources when reporting facts? Are the author's sources from credible organizations?

4. **Does the presented evidence completely support the claim?**

   Might there be other information that could support or discredit the message? Does the author make logical inferences and conclusions from the evidence presented in the article?

5. **Who is the target audience of this message?**

   How is this message directed at this particular audience?

6. **Is the message promoting certain values, lifestyles, positions, or ideas either directly or indirectly?**

   Are there any positions or ideas that are being promoted that are not explicit in the message?

Evaluating Internet Sources

Imagine that you want to search the Internet to find out about the effectiveness of vitamin supplements so that you can come to your own conclusion. When you are searching for information online, a search engine is searching from over one trillion websites.[1] Determining which websites and sources of information are reliable and which are biased is difficult. To make an informed decision about this topic, you will need to identify accurate and unbiased websites. Below is a suggested list of questions that will help you determine if a particular website is an accurate and unbiased source of information.

1. **Are the authors' names, contact information, and credentials clearly labeled on the website?**

   Accurate websites will usually contain information from knowledgeable authors who have their names, credentials, and contact information clearly labeled on the website. Some websites are managed by a collection of people or an organization, and information on the exact author may not be clearly stated. However,

---

1. Alpert, Jesse & Hajaj, Nissan. (July 25, 2008). We knew the Web was big. . . .
The Official Google Blog. Retrieved August 2010 from http://googleblog.blogspot.om
/2008/07/we-knew-web-was-big.html.

these organizations should state the names, contact information, and credentials somewhere on their website of the people who represent the organization.

2. **Is the information and the website up to date?**

   Some information that you may be seeking needs to be current. For example, if you were looking for the number of cars in the United States, you would want the most recent data. A study conducted in 1982 would not be helpful in this case. When seeking information that needs to be current, determine if the date the article or information was written is clearly indicated on the website so you can be sure you are accessing the most recent information. Credible websites will usually indicate the date the article or information was created or last updated. Also, the person or organization maintaining the website should be regularly updating the website, so that the majority of links to other websites work.

3. **Are sources of information clearly cited?**

   When factual information is stated in a website, is the source clearly cited so you can refer back to it?

4. **Are there links to more resources on this topic?**

   Authoritative websites will often provide links to further information from other sources that support their claim. Authors of websites that contain information that is biased or inaccurate usually do not provide additional information that supports their claims.

5. **What are other people saying about the author or the organization that produced this information?**

   If you come across information from an author or organization that you are unfamiliar with, perform a search for other information about the author or organization. What are experts writing about the author's or organization's other work?

6. **Why is this website on the Internet?**

   Was this information put on the Internet to inform or to persuade people? Is the author selling something? What is the author's motivation for providing this information?

Further Resources

Thier, M., & Daviss, B. (2002). The new science literacy. Portsmouth, NH: Heinemann.

Center for Media Literacy. http://www.medialit.org.

PBS Teachers. Media literacy. http://www.pbs.org/teachers/media_lit.

Crosscutting Concepts

PATTERNS	A pattern is a set of repeating things or events. Scientists observe patterns in their data. Patterns lead to questions about relationships and ideas about what causes these relationships.
CAUSE AND EFFECT A → B	Events have causes. If "A" causes "B" to happen, they have a cause-and-effect relationship. A major activity of science is to explain how this happens. Sometime the causes are simple and sometimes they are complex. Sometimes both A and B occur, but one does not cause the other.
SCALE, PROPORTION, AND QUANTITY	Scientific phenomena occur at various scales of size, time, and energy. Phenomena observed at one scale may not be observable at another scale. Scientists use proportional relationships to compare measurements of objects and events. They often use mathematical expressions and equations to represent these relationships.
SYSTEM AND SYSTEM MODELS	A system is a group of interacting objects or processes. Describing a system, including its components, interactions and boundaries, and making models of that system helps scientists and engineers understand phenomena and test ideas.
ENERGY AND MATTER	Tracking changes of energy and matter into, out of, and within systems helps scientists understand the systems' possibilities and limitations. Many cause and effect relationships result from changes of energy and matter.
STRUCTURE AND FUNCTION	The structure (shape, composition, construction) of an object or living thing determines many of its properties and functions (what the structure can do).
STABILITY AND CHANGE y / x	For natural and built systems alike, conditions are sometimes stable (the same or within a range), and sometimes they change. Scientists study what conditions lead to either stability or change.

Glossary

aquifer A rock layer that allows groundwater to flow through it and collect.

aquitard A rock layer that restricts the flow of groundwater.

asthenosphere The weak, soft solid layer of the mantle 100–250 km below Earth's surface.

continental drift The idea that the continents were once joined together to form a single large continent, which over time broke up and slowly moved great distances apart.

convection The transfer of thermal energy by the movement of matter of different temperatures.

convergent plate boundary A region where lithospheric plates move towards each other.

divergent plate boundary A region where lithospheric plates are spreading apart.

earthquake A sudden release of energy in Earth's interior, which can cause shaking at the surface.

evidence Information that supports or refutes a claim.

geological time Time periods of thousands, millions, and billions of years.

GPS (Global Positioning System) A network of satellites around Earth that communicate with GPS receivers located on the ground.

gravity A natural phenomenon that causes objects to be pulled toward each other.

groundwater Water found underground in the spaces and cracks within earth materials.

igneous rock Rock that forms when magma or lava cools and solidifies.

landslide The movement of rock, soil, and other earth materials down a slope.

lava Hot, liquid rock on Earth's surface.

lithosphere The solid layer of Earth's crust and upper mantle.

lithospheric plates Sections of Earth's lithosphere.

magma Hot, liquid rock under Earth's surface.

magnitude The size of an earthquake.

metamorphic rock Rock that has changed due to extreme heat and/or pressure.

mid-ocean ridge A large underwater volcanic mountain chain.

model Any representation of a system (or its components) used to help one understand and communicate how it works.

natural hazard A naturally occurring event that may negatively affect people and the environment.

nonrenewable resource A natural resource that cannot be replaced faster than it is used up by human populations.

nuclear waste The leftover radioactive material produced by reactors at nuclear power plants, nuclear medical treatments, and nuclear research and technology facilities.

plate boundary Where two or more of Earth's lithospheric plates meet.

plate tectonics The theory that the Earth's lithospheric plates are in constant motion.

renewable resource A natural resource that can be replaced or replenished faster than it is used up by human populations.

rock cycle The process that describes how one type of rock becomes another.

sediment Parts of rocks, shell, and dead organisms that have been worn down into small pieces.

sedimentary rock Layers of hardened sediment.

subduction The process of one plate being pulled below another plate.

thermal energy Internal energy of a substance due to the movement of particles within the substance.

trade-off A desirable outcome given up to gain another desirable outcome.

transform plate boundary A region where two plates move past each other.

trench A deep, narrow depression on the sea floor.

volcano An opening in Earth's surface through which lava, gas, and ash escape from magma underground.

Index

Bold page number indicates a definition. *Italic* page number indicates an illustration.

L

landslide hazards, map of the U.S., *110*

landslides
> definition, **155**
> Gorkha, Nepal (2015), 20, *20*
> modeling, 15–16
> Puerto Rico (2017), *15*

lava. *See also* magma.
> definition, **155**
> measuring the movement of, *69*
> pillow lavas, *79*
> solidified, 26

less-gassy magma, 26–27

line graphs, 132–133

liquid, measuring the volume of, 128

literacy strategies
> communication skills, 148
> concept maps, 147
> Internet sources, evaluating, 151–152
> keeping a notebook, 144–145
> media messages, evaluating,
> > 149–151, *150*
> oral presentations, 142
> reading scientific procedures, 143
> writing a formal investigation report,
> > 146

lithosphere, **47**, **155**

lithospheric plates
> boundaries. *See* plate boundaries.
> definition, **47**, **155**
> maps, *47*, *48*
> movement, 59–62. *See also* plate
> > tectonics.

Loihi Island, forming, 70

M

magma. *See also* lava.
> definition, **17**, **155**
> less-gassy, 26–27
> more-gassy, 27–29
> solidified, 25

magnitude, **53**, **155**

Mammoth Mountain volcanic eruption,
> *22*

mantle, **46**

mapping
> earthquakes, 31–33
> the ocean floor, 116
> volcanoes, 31–33

maps
> earthquakes, *63*
> lithospheric plates, *47*, *48*
> Ring of Fire, 63, *63*
> of volcanic eruptions, *63*
> worldwide earthquakes and
> > volcanoes, *48*

maps of the U.S.
> aquifers, *111*
> earthquake hazards, *110*
> granite outcrops, *95*, *111*
> landslide hazards, *110*
> locations of operating nuclear
> > reactors, *7*, *109*
> metal ore mines, *112*
> oil and natural gas production, *98*
> population density by county, *6*, *109*
> volcano hazards, *111*

matter, tracking, 153

measuring the volume of a liquid, 128

media literacy, 149–151, *150*

metal ore mines, map of the U.S., *112*

metal ores, *96*

metamorphic rock
> definition, **92**, **155**
> formation of, 116

metric system
> base units, 139–140
> prefixes, 140
> SI (International System of Units),
> > 139–140

Mexico City earthquake (2017), *31*

microscopes
> drawing microscopic views, 138, *138*
> focusing, 137
> parts of, *137*
> safety guidelines, 137–138

Mid-Atlantic Ridge, *65*

mid-ocean ridges
> definition, **65**, **155**
> diagram of, *64*
> Mid-Atlantic Ridge, *65*
> summary of, 116

model, definition, **15**, **155**

modeling
> earthquakes, 53–57
> landslides, 15–16
> systems, **153**
> volcanoes, 25–29

more-gassy magma, 27–29

Credits

Abbreviations: t (top), m (middle), b (bottom), l (left), r (right), c (center)

All illustrations by Seventeenth Street Studios

Front cover photo and unit opener: LukaKikina/Shutterstock; Page 3: Avda; Page 5 l: Corbis, r: ©Tim Wright / Corbis; Page 9: Denis R. LeBlanc, USGS; Page 15: Yuisa Rios/FEMA; Page 17 l: R.E. Wallace/United States Geological Survey, r: ©Reuters/Corbis; Page 19: Simon Young/CaribRM; Page 20: USGS; Page 21: Joseph Rosenbaum/USGS; Page 22: USGS; Page 31 l: K. Ciryem, r: AntoFran; Page 35 l: USGPS, r: USGS; Page 47: M. Chuck; Page 53: Claudio Núñez; Page 59: Image Science and Analysis Laboratory, NASA, Johnson Space Center; Page 68 t: US Archiv ARCWEB, b: Eve Fraser; Page 69: USGS Page 71: ©Tepco/Jana Press; Page 73: Richard Paselk, Humboldt State University Natural History Museum; Page 79: NOAA Okeanos Explorer Program; Page 93: Eric Guinther; Page 94: David Iliff; Page 96: Jonathan Zander; Page 98: RSMultimedia/Alamy Stock Photo 101: NASA